Jack Tales
And Mountain Yarns
As Told By Orville Hicks

TRANSCRIPTION AND TEXT BY
JULIA TAYLOR EBEL

ILLUSTRATION BY
SHERRY JENKINS JENSEN

—— AFTERWORD BY THOMAS McGOWAN ——

Parkway Publishers, Inc.
Boone, North Carolina

Library of Congress Cataloging-in-Publication Data

Hicks, Orville.
Jack tales and mountain yarns : as told by Orville Hicks / transcribed and edited by Julia Taylor Ebel ; illustrated by Sherry Jensen.
p. cm.
Summary: "Orville Hicks has enthralled audiences beyond the porches of Beech Mountain, North Carolina, for more than two decades. Jack Tales and Mountain Yarns captures the voice of the master storyteller in more than twenty transcribed stories, paired with lively pencil sketches. Having grown up in a hollow, he knows the mountain setting and his clever character Jack"—Provided by publisher.
ISBN 978-1-933251-64-6 (hard cover) — ISBN 978-1-933251-65-3 (soft cover)
1. Jack tales. 2. Tall tales. 3. Hicks, Orville. I. Ebel, Julia Taylor. II. Title.
GR105.37.J32H53 2009
398.2--dc22
2008039559

Photography by Julia Taylor Ebel

Book Design by Aaron Burleson, spokesmedia

"The Hardest Whipping": Mountain Dew and Pepsi are trademarks of PepsiCo, Inc.
The illustration of the Mountain Dew bottle is used with permission of PepsiCo, Inc.

In memory of Mama

—OH

❧

To John,
to all who keep the stories of their people,
and to that rascal Jack, wherever he is.

—JTE

❧

To my sons,
Taylor, Trevor, and Nicholas

—SJJ

ACKNOWLEDGMENTS:

My heartfelt thanks to Orville and Sylvia Hicks, gracious and enthusiastic teammates on this project and true friends. What fun we have had! Thanks to Orville's family—sons and daughters-in-law, brothers and sisters, cousins, nephews, nieces—all who offered me windows into Orville's world.

Thanks to Dr. Thomas McGowan of Appalachian State University, Department of English, who has studied and laughed with Orville for years. I value both his insight into mountain language and lore and his blessing on this project.

Thanks to Sherry Jensen, who blends enthusiasm and artistic skill on these pages; to my publisher, Rao Aluri, who enables and encourages me to keep these stories; and to Aaron Burleson, who takes all the pieces and makes a beautiful book.

Thanks to my husband, Alan, and to my son John, who put up with my efforts. They know these stories should be kept. Thanks to Alan for technical support and for traveling with me—and sometimes Orville—to Boone, Raleigh, Charleston, and more. Thanks to John, who speaks of the importance of narratives and of seeing our place in our own narratives, which thread through generations of our histories.

—JTE

CONTENTS:

A *yarn* is a tale, especially an exaggerated tale.
To *spin a yarn* is to tell a tale.
A *yarnspinner* is a storyteller.
Orville Hicks is a yarnspinner,
a teller of the Appalachian Mountain tales of his people.

A Heritage of Stories

A listener can hardly help being drawn into a story told by Orville Hicks. Orville's laughter spills out with his stories—laughter that rolls out from somewhere deep inside. He could not keep it in if he had to. His mountain tales are as fresh today as when his mother, Sarah Harmon Hicks, told them to her children while they sat together on the porch to shell peas or to tie galax leaves into bunches. When they had gathered and tied 1,000 galax leaves, they could sell them to the floral market for about 50 cents, but stories told over their work are still priceless.

Orville Hicks came by storytelling naturally. He, along with his ten brothers and sisters, grew up in a hollow by Beech Mountain, North Carolina, in the 1950s and 1960s. Orville was the youngest. The Hicks children heard their mother's tales. She had heard them from her father, McKeller (Kell) Harmon, who had heard them from his father, Council (Counce) Harmon. Council Harmon had a reputation as a yarnspinner. Tales of him depict a tall, lively man who liked to talk and liked to dance. He was said to have stopped often to talk and to tell tales as he walked the mountain roads.

Folklorist Richard Chase discovered the treasure of folklore around Beech Mountain in the 1930s. He recorded a number of descendants of Council Harmon as he gathered stories for his books, *Jack Tales* and *Grandfather Tales*. Kell Harmon and Sarah Harmon Hicks were among the storytellers whom Chase recorded.

Orville heard stories of the clever mountain boy Jack and other tales not only from his mother but also from others around Beech Mountain, including his second cousin Ray Hicks and his uncle Adie Harmon. While each teller offered a slant on the stories, the basic stories remained as familiar tales.

Orville continues this rich tradition of storytelling. Those who hear his tales will notice a ring of authenticity in his words and voice. They will glimpse a mountain boy's intimacy with the woods surrounding the family farm. They will see his humble lifestyle in his characters, including Jack. Orville understands Jack, for he himself has been Jack. When faced with a challenge in younger years, Orville sometimes paused to think, now what would Jack do?

With unfailing good humor, Orville Hicks weaves story and life into tales for all ages. Orville is a keeper of stories and of his rich mountain heritage. Stories are so much a part of Orville that any conversation with him is likely to evolve into a story of Jack or a slice of mountain life. Orville brings his listeners a piece of the past, a past that will be remembered as long as the tales of his people are told. For keeping his Appalachian Mountain storytelling tradition, the North Carolina Arts Council honored Orville with the coveted North Carolina Heritage Award in 2007.

The home and porch where Orville's mother told and retold tales are gone now, but Orville often visits the Beech Mountain home of traditional storyteller Ray Hicks. Ray died in 2003, but his family remains at their homestead. At Ray's home, Orville often listened to Ray's tales and learned stories about Jack. As naturally as the morning mist rises from the hollows, stories still rise from Ray's porch. Orville is keeping these stories alive not only in public tellings but also on porches, on mountaintops, and around woodstoves or kerosene heaters—wherever two or more are gathered.

Yet for all that storytelling, there is no pretense in Orville Hicks. He is as real as they come.

The stories that follow are transcriptions of Orville's words. The stories keep his words with minor editing for clarity. A glossary at the back of the book explains Orville's expressions and pronunciations. The poetic line form reflects the rhythms of his speech. Listen for Orville's voice in the printed words. Hear the runs and pauses of voice as he draws his listener into the stories. Imagine his laughter punctuating the tales. Picture his hands rising, falling, stretching wide, drawing listeners into his tales.

So gather 'round.

Imagine that you are there,

sitting on the old porch.

Gather 'round and listen.

Listen as Orville tells his stories.

Listen to the voices of his ancestors

whispering from the mountain hollows,

speaking through stories.

Listen.

Growing-Up Stories, Riddles, and Songs

Stories abounded in the hollow where Orville Hicks grew up. Life in the shadows of Beech Mountain offered a mountain boy plenty of space to explore and plenty of opportunities to find stories in his own experience. Mountain people swapped tales over farm work and spun yarns on the porch or by the woodstove as they finished the day's work.

Mountain people have passed along their wisdom, warnings, and philosophies not only in stories but also in songs, sayings, and superstitions. Ballads often tell fateful tales of forbidden love. As such, they are cautionary songs. Other folksongs entertained, and riddles, frequently posed by his mother, playfully challenged Orville and his brothers and sisters to solve the puzzles.

Orville talks about his Appalachian childhood and tells a number of stories about growing up in the mountains—some old, some crafted from his own mountain experience; some true, some stretching truth. He draws from his youthful years on the farm in the hollow and from his days in the woods. He still sings the old songs, and he enjoys the challenge of old riddles as well as new jokes.

As Orville tells stories, he often weaves longer traditional tales with shorter ones or with personal stories of growing up in the mountains. Listen for clever shifts in the rhythms of Orville's voice as his stories dance between truth and fiction and as he blends the two.

GATHERING HERBS AND STORIES

*H*erbs was a big part of our life.
        We'd sell them and help us get through the winter.
They helped pay the bills and helped put food on the table—
helped put flour and sugar on the table,
helped pay taxes on the house we owed every year,
helped pay the light bill after we got lights.

        Mama'd get up in the morning.
She'd say, "Young'uns, I'm going over there in Bear Waller and pull galax.
I'll be home this evening."

        We was real small—couldn't go with her.
Some of the older ones would stay around the house.
Maybe Daddy'd be around the house, working in the fields.

        Me and Mary and Jerry would be setting on the porch waiting for Mama.
She'd be gone all day, and we'd miss her.
We'd see her coming across the mountains, a big old sack of galax on her back.
And you could see she was about gived out.

        Daddy'd still be out in the field or something.
He'd sometimes be pretty late before he got in.

        And Mama'd pour them galax on the porch.
And every time, she'd have us some mountain tea in there to chew on,
or she'd have a little rabbit she'd caught in the woods

or a little old bitty terrapin turtle.

And she'd sit on the porch, and we'd sit down beside of her.

   She'd say, "Young'uns, I can make you say 'who.'"

   "No, you can't neither, Mama. You can't do it."

   "Well, I don't guess I can."

She said, "I know someone down the road that can."

   And we'd say, "Who, Mama? Who?"

She'd get us every time.

   By the time I was seven, I was out pulling galax with Mama.

I probably played more than I pulled at first.

In the evening, we'd have to bunch the galax we pulled that day.

Mama'd bring a big old sack full of galax and put 'em on the porch

and pour 'em out.

Then she'd get in her chair,

and she'd get a thread she tied the galax with.

Me and Mary and Jerry would count—twenty-five leaves to bunch.

Mama'd put 'em between her knees and tie 'em and keep on telling the tales.

   When I was bigger enough to put a hoe in my hand,

we'd be out in the garden,

hoeing a row of corn or hauling potatoes or digging 'taters.

I always liked it barefoot. That warm dirt wiggling between your toes felt good.

Sometimes Mama'd look back and see us young'uns falling behind.

She'd tell us a tale or sometimes sing a song,

and we'd work faster to catch up to her.

   Mama and Daddy kept a garden. They'd plant peas, corn, onions,

tomatoes, mustard, cucumber, squash.

They kept lettuce and turnips—I mean about everything you could grow.

In the fall of the year, we'd gather 'taters and turnips and pumpkins,

and we'd put them in the cellar.

We had a whole bunch of apple trees on the farm.

We'd pick the apples and put them in the cellar.
We'd pick the peas and the beans, and Mama'd can all of them.
        We kept a horse.
Kept a hunting dog.
Mama kept a cat.
The chickens give us eggs to eat,
and the cow give us milk.
The hogs give us meat in the fall of the year.
        Hog killing time come and people'd come help us.
Most times people just swapped work.
Back then, people didn't have no money, so they traded work for work.
A lot of times, we done it to be together.
Didn't cost nobody a dime.
        We'd buy flour, baking soda, sugar, and maybe salt—things like that—
at Mast's Store to get through the winter.
Probably kerosene.
When we got a little older,
sometimes Mama'd send us to the little store over at Matney.
It took a good hour to walk there
unless Bill Eller's dog got after us. Then we'd go a little faster.
        But really, we had about everything at home.
We never got out from up there where we lived much.
The young'uns stayed basically at home
until they got bigger enough to leave home.

        Mama sung a lot of old ballads.
She sung "Pretty Polly" a lot
and "Sweet William."
She sung a lot of gospel songs.
She had an old banjo she played, mostly in the evening times.

She sung "Old Joe Clark."

And she sung "Lazy John."

Some other people sung it "Soldier John."

      Mama took time out. She'd give you riddles and tell you a tale

or maybe sing you a song.

I think the girls learned the songs more than the boys did.

I liked the Jack Tales.

      I learned most of my tales from Mama.

You know, we growed up with no television,

no electricity in the house until 1964, and so

most of the evening time was storytelling time.

Hearing tales was just part of growing up in the fifties and sixties.

I'd milk the cow, and we'd get our chores done;

and Mama would holler, "You young'uns want to hear a tale?"

Before bedtime, we'd sit on the porch there.

Sometimes we'd break beans

or shell peas

or bunch galax.

And Mama'd sit there and tell us a tale or two before bedtime.

Really, that's how I learned 'em, just listening to Mama.

I liked the tales so good.

I just sit there and listened to her and learned 'em that way.

      She told the tales straight to me.

She'd heared it from her daddy and her grandpa.

And it was just passed on down through the family.

So it'd been in the family so many years,

it just come down to the next generation—the one I was in.

      I never went to school to learn tales.

I was just going through the mountain, listening to the mountain people,

walking the trails, doing what Jack would do.

Everywhere we went, we had to walk.
I just tell the tales like I remember from Mama.
The tales have been handed down through the family.
They just kept a-going.

  Uncle Adie Harmon used to sing a lot of ballads.
He kept a banjo about all his life and played.
I'd help my cousin Benny do the chores.
Sometimes Uncle Adie'd tell us part of the tale.
He'd say come back next week, young'uns, and I'll finish the tale.

  The tales didn't vary that much in the mountains—just a little, I guess.
I'd be hearing pretty much the same story.
They'd be just a little difference in 'em.
The people who'd tell it might stretch it a little bit.
We didn't have that much range of mountains to go through.
They told the tales pretty much the same way.

  What was special about Ray Hicks was the way he told the tales
and the way he talked.
Ray and Rosa'd come down to the house with the young'uns.
And I'd hear him tell about things that'd happened in the mountains—
and I didn't know if it was true or not.
It was exciting sitting there watching Ray.
You'd have to listen real careful.

  Growing up on that farm,
raising our food,
pulling herbs—
that's pretty much how we lived.
It was a good life.
A real good life.

*Green in the summer
and brown in the fall.
Sweet in the middle.
Bitter as gall.*

What is it?
  (A walnut)

SQUIRREL HUNTING

Growing up there in the mountains,
I liked to hunt a lot.

One day I took my old shotgun
and went out in the woods squirrel hunting.
I hunted and hunted till about twelve o'clock and didn't see nothing,
and I begin to get hungry.

Well, I looked out and
they was a big field out there.
And right in the middle of that field was a blackberry patch.
And, gosh, they was big old blackberries growing out there!

I laid my gun up against the tree,
walked out in the middle of that field, and begun to eat them blackberries.

About ten minutes eating blackberries, I heared something behind me.

Grrrrr! Grrrrr!

Looked behind me and there stood a big old bear,
and I knowed—the way it was looking at me—it wanted to eat me for its dinner.
And I looked up in the woods, and I seen my gun
about three hundred foot out in the woods
up against a tree.

I looked out in the middle of that field,
and they was one tree in the middle of that field—
the only tree around.
I looked again,
and the bottom limb on that tree was a hundred foot off the ground.
    But I took at that tree hard as I could run,
and that bear took out behind me.
I was running hard as I could run, and I knowed good and well
when I got to that tree,
if I didn't make that limb the first jump,
I was a goner.
    Well, I got to that tree.
That bear was right behind me.
And I jumped hard as I could jump,
and I missed that limb slicker'n a whistle.
But I'll let you all know one thing.
I caught it coming back down.

I hunted squirrels all through the mountains.
I never encountered a bear, but I encountered a panther one time,
over there in what we called Hickory Patch—
two baby panthers and a mama one.
I had enough sense to stay quiet, and they went on by.
I was about thirteen or fourteen.
But Daddy told us not to waste shells.
If we couldn't eat it, we didn't shoot it.

From OLD JOE CLARK

Old Joe Clark had an old mule.
His name was Morgan Brown.
And every tooth in that mule's head
Was forty inches round.

Get along home, Old Joe Clark.
Get along home, I say.
Get along home, Old Joe Clark.
Tomorrow's another day.

Old Joe Clark, he had an old cow,
And she was mule-y born.
It took a jaybird forty-eight hours
To fly from horn to horn.

Get along home, Old Joe Clark.
Get along home, I say.
Get along home, Old Joe Clark.
Tomorrow's another day.

I went over to Old Joe Clark's.
Never been there before.
He slept on the feather bed.
Made me sleep on the floor.

Get along home, Old Joe Clark.
Get along home, I say.
Get along home, Old Joe Clark.
Tomorrow's another day.

Folksong

*Do you know what color
Old Joe's yellow turkey is?*

THE MULE EGGS

*N*ow, we lived way back up in the mountains there.
    My daddy raised a lot of pumpkins.
It come fall of the year,
and we'd sell pumpkins to people for Thanksgiving or maybe for Halloween.
But we lived off down in the holler.
    The old road that come down in the holler was a pretty rough road,
but the main road that went by up there was a pretty good road,
and a lot of people'd come buy a pumpkin.
If they even had a car back then, they'd park on the top of the hill,
walk down in the holler where we lived at and buy a pumpkin,
and walk back out.
    And one Saturday,
my daddy left me down in that holler at the barn
selling these pumpkins all by myself.
Well, along about one o'clock,
I heared a racket.
I looked up.
Here come a big old Cadillac up there at the road.
Gosh, the feller got out of the car
had a big suit on,
a big old necktie.

He looked like a rich fellow. I knowed he wasn't from around here.

But he seen me down at the barn.

He walked down there where I was at.

He looked at me.

He looked down at them pumpkins

and looked back at me,

and he said, "Son, what are them things?"

I knowed a man didn't know what a pumpkin was,

I had me a sucker right then.

So I told him they was mule eggs.

He said, "Mule eggs?"

I said, "Yeah, take 'em home and keep 'em warm."

I said, "About two weeks, you bust it open, a little old baby mule'll jump out."

He said, "Go-o-osh, I been wanting a baby mule."

He said, "How much are they?"

I said, "Twenty dollars."

He said, "Son, give me that big one right there."

Well, he got the biggest pumpkin we had, and he put it on his back.

And he cloom up the hill.

Got in his car and drove off.

Well, about two weeks went by,

and I done plumb forgot about it.

My daddy left me down at the barn selling them pumpkins again

all by myself.

Well, long about one o'clock, I looked up,

and here come that same car.

That fellow got out and he looked awful mad.

He seen me and here he come.

He got down there where I was at, and he said,

"Son, that mule egg you sold me wasn't no good.

I took it home. We kept it warm for two weeks."

He said, "I sat on it for a week.

Got my wife to sit on it for a week.

We busted it open. We didn't see no baby mule in it."

I said, "You must've got hold of a bad'un."

I said, "You can have one more for half price."

He said, "Well, well, well, I guess I could try one more."

He got another big pumpkin, put it on his back.

Cloom up the hill and got nearly to his car,

and I heared him a-hollering.

I looked up,

and that pumpkin fell off his back and was rolling back down the hill.

Here come that pumpkin by me and that man a-chasing it.

The pumpkin hit the bottom of the hill,

and it rolled in the briar patch.

When it hit the briar patch, it busted open.

And a big old jackrabbit jumped out of that briar patch.

That man seen that jackrabbit

and thought it was a baby mule come out of that pumpkin.

He took after it running, hollering,

"Whoa! Whoa! Come back here!
You belong to me! Whoa! Whoa!"

He run after that rabbit this way and that a-way.

About a hour, he come back,

his tongue lolled out.

He said, "Son, you can keep your mule eggs."

I said, "Why?"

He said, "That little devil's that fast when it's little,

when it got grown, I wouldn't be able to catch it and plow with it anyway."

So if anybody'd like a mule egg, I'll sell 'em one.

20

Grandpa And The Hand Glider

Now, growing up there in the mountains,
my grandpa and grandma lived above me up on the mountain,
there on top of the hill.
And back in them times, nobody had never seen a hand glider before—
didn't know what one was.
And one come over Grandpa's house a-flying one day.
And he grabbed his shotgun.
He grabbed it and shot at the hand glider.

Grandma runned out and hollered, *"Did you get it?"*
Grandpa said, "No, but it turned that man loose it had a-hold of."

ASHCAKES AND CORN FLITTERS

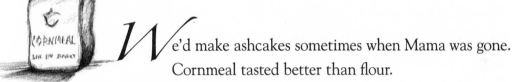

We'd make ashcakes sometimes when Mama was gone.
Cornmeal tasted better than flour.
We'd make 'em out of flour sometimes.
We just put cornmeal in water.
That was about all we had.
Most times cornmeal was already salted.
We'd get it and kinda roll it up like a ball.
Just put it in the ashes in the fireplace or the wood stove.
        After it cooked in the ashes,
you could break it apart and eat the middle.
It was kinda like cornbread in the middle of it.
It was real good—
had a good flavor to it.
It'd turn black, but the insides would cook,
and it was delicious.
Sometime I'd eat the ashes and all.
        After we was married, I tried some in tinfoil.
It cooked better.
        We'd put 'taters down there in the ashes
and cook them like that, the same way.
Cook them in the ashes,

then bust 'em open
and eat 'em.

 We'd make corn flitters too.
Just take flour and mix it up with water.
Put corn—juice and all—in with it.
Sometimes we put an egg in it—if we got some.
Back then, we probably didn't.
Put a little lard in the pan.
Then put the flitter in the pan on the stove.
Pour a little in the pan, kinda like a little pancake.
Flatten it out.
Then cook it, turn it over, and put another one in the pan.

 We'd make 'tater biscuits like that, the same way—
put 'taters in it.
But I like the corn ones better.
They have a better flavor.

 Food seemed like it tasted better back then—
come off'n them old wood stoves.

Big at the bottom,
little at the top.
Something in the middle
goes flippity-flop.

What is it?
 (A butter churn)

THE HARDEST WHIPPING

*N*ow, living up there in the mountains—
when we growed up there—we never did have no car.

Daddy never did have no driver's license.

So a sody pop and a candy bar was something we usually got for Christmas.

Me and Mary and Jerry was at home.

We'd been working in the fields all week long. We'd been working hard—
gathering beans and 'taters and stuff.

My oldest brother lived down in Siler City.

He'd come up,

and he had an old—I believe it was, if I'm not mistaken—'52 Chevrolet.

I heared Daddy tell him, he said,

"Let's take them young'uns up to the store and buy 'em a sody pop."

Well, we got in my brother's car.

About three mile up the road there

was a little old store

we went to a lot.

We'd walk to it if our brother or nobody wasn't around to give us a ride.

We got up to that store,

and it was about the time, I think,

that Mountain Dew come in the mountains.

They was a big sign hanging on the store.

It showed a man with a Mountain Dew bottle shooting through his hat.

And I kept looking at that sign.

And Daddy got to the store,

and he looked back and he said, "What kind of drink do you young'uns want?"

Mary said, "Get me a Pepsi."

Jerry said, "Get me a Pepsi too, Daddy."

Daddy said, "Orville, what kind do you want?"

I said, "Daddy,

get me one of them good old Mountain Dews while you're in there."

Well, my daddy turned around and walked back to the car,

and he pulled me out of the back seat

and got a little switch off'n the tree there.

And I got one of the hardest whippings I believe I ever got in my life

there at that little old store.

When he got done whipping me, he said, "Son,

don't you ne-e-ever, never mention moonshine around your Daddy again!"

Potato On A Stick

Now growing up there in the mountains,
    us children,
most times when we wanted to have fun,
we had to make do ourselves.
    We used to go out and get a long stick.
A birch stick was best.
Oh, I'd say it'd be
five or six foot long.
We'd get to the top of the mountain,
we'd put a apple on it.
We could sling a apple about half a mile
back down in the holler.
We'd get up there and play all day
to see who could sling the apple the farthest.
    Well, one Saturday,
it come 'tater digging time. We was digging 'taters.
And Daddy was at the lower end of the 'tater field with the old mule,
plowing the 'taters out.
We'd done plowed the upper part out.

We was up there picking them up.
I happened to have that old stick in my back pocket
that I slung them apples on.
    I reached down and found me a pretty-good-sized round 'tater.
I put it on the end of that stick,
and I slung it kind of to the right, hard as I could sling it.
The 'tater went to the left.
It flew off the stick—went down there and hit Daddy in the back of the head.
And it busted.
When it busted,
I took off a-running.
    Daddy caught me after I tore about a acre of corn down.
He took me out to the woodshed
and said, "Son,
I'm gonna whip you."
He said, "I ain't gonna whip you for hitting me."
He said, "I'm gonna whip you for wasting food like that."
    I knowed good and well
he give me a couple of licks for hitting him too.
I can still feel that whipping.

*In the old days, people had corn shuckings. Neighbors
would come help shuck your field and stack the stalks
in the shocks. Boys would bring their girlfriends. If
somebody shucked a red ear of corn, he got to kiss his
girlfriend. Everybody'd stop and watch.*

From SOURWOOD MOUNTAIN

Chickens crowing on Sourwood Mountain.
Hey-ho, doodle-um-day.
So many pretty girls, I can't count them.
Hey-ho, doodle-um-day.

My true love lives up the holler.
She won't come and I won't follow.
Hey-ho, doodle-um-day.

My true love is a blue-eyed daisy.
If I don't get her, I go crazy.
Hey-ho, doodle-um-day.

Chickens crowing on Sourwood Mountain.
Hey-ho, doodle-um-day.

Old man, old man, I want your daughter.
Hey-ho, doodle-um-day.
What do you want her for, boy?
To bake my bread and carry my water.
Hey-ho, doodle-um-day.

Chickens crowing on Sourwood Mountain.
Hey-ho, doodle-um-day.

Folksong

A man went to church on Sunday.
He stayed three days
and came back on Sunday.

How did he do that?
          (His horse's name was Sunday.)

29

BROOM STRAWS AND SWEETHEARTS

 here used to be a saying about putting a broom straw
under your bed to find out who you'll marry.

Mama used to tell us that's how you found your sweetheart—
or the one you're gonna marry.

Take a glass of water.
Put it under the bed you sleep in,
and put a broom straw across that glass of water
under the bed.
And that night
you'll dream you're on a bridge—
water running under it.
You look on the other side.
If you're a boy,
you'll see the girl you're gonna marry;
but if you're a girl, you'll see the man you're gonna marry
standing on the other side of the bridge.

If you'd put that glass of water and broom straw under your bed,
it'd come true.

If you raise your feet up and let somebody sweep under you feet,
you'll never get married.

LAZY JOHN

"Lazy John, lazy John,
When you gonna marry me?"
"How can I marry you, my pretty little miss,
With me no shoes to wear?"

Up she jumped, and away she went
Down to the market square.
Bought the prettiest pair of shoes money could buy
For lazy John to wear.

"Lazy John, lazy John,
When you gonna marry me?"
"How can I marry you, my pretty little miss,
With me no britches to wear?"

Up she jumped, and away she went
Down to the market square.
Bought the finest britches money could buy
For lazy John to wear.

"Lazy John, lazy John,
When you gonna marry me?"
"How can I marry you, my pretty little miss,
With me no shirt to wear?"

Up she jumped, and away she went
Down to the market square.
Bought the finest shirt money could buy
For lazy John to wear.

"Lazy John, lazy John,
When you gonna marry me?"
"How can I marry you, my pretty little miss,
With me no hat to wear?"

Up she jumped, and away she went
Down to the market square.
Bought the finest hat money could buy
For lazy John to wear.

"Lazy John, lazy John,
Now you gonna marry me?"
"How can I marry such an ugly miss,
With all these fine clothes to wear?"

Jack Tales

Who but Jack would dare say to a powerful king or a fierce giant, "Wait a minute"? The likeable character Jack appears in a number of folktales. Jack represents many clever persons who must rely on their own wits to survive against larger-than-life dangers and evil powers. Even with his life threatened, Jack remains calm. His quick and clever thinking saves him from one jam after another despite the odds. Time after time, Jack outwits dangerous giants, powerful kings, wild animals, and his tricky brothers, Tom and Will.

Jack Tales are rooted in Europe, but Southern Appalachian Mountain folk have told the tales for generations. As Orville spins his ancestors' yarns, the stories reflect the mountain way of life while honoring the European roots. Jack is a poor mountain boy in the stories. The mountain settings in tales reflect the homes familiar to storytellers who settled in Appalachia and to the generations who continued to tell the stories. The king as a character comes from the European roots of earlier storytellers.

Jack's adventures span a broad period of his life. In some tales, he is a young boy with his mama. In several tales, he wins a young lady's hand in marriage. The repeated marriages of the young man Jack raise the question of Jack's identity. Was he a single character or a representative of many clever mountain boys? One tale, "Sheepskin," highlights his wife's cunning. (Another tale told by Orville but not included in this collection, begins with a much older Jack, soon before his death.) Through generations of storytellers, Jack survives danger again and again and leaves the world safer and happier. He is the hero of the mountain folktales.

The collection that follows is a sample of Orville's stories about the clever Jack. Jack also appears in other tales told in mountain communities beyond Beech Mountain. Many of these Jack Tales have been told in regions to which descendants of Orville's great-grandfather, Council Harmon, moved and told stories.

Jack

ORVILLE ON JACK

Jack growed up about the time I did—pretty close.

Mama told us a lot of Jack Tales—
and Ray.

Most times when Ray told the Jack Tales, we'd go up to his house.

Ray'd get to telling a Jack Tale.

His big arms would come out.

When Ray got done telling a tale, you was in the tale with Jack.

He'd tell "Jack's Hunting Trip,"

and next thing you knew,

you'd have your gun and be about out there hunting with Jack.

Jack was clever, witty, smart.

Jack was an old mountain boy,

but he had a lot of sense.

See, Jack was just a ordinary boy.

But when it come right down to it, he could outwit the king.

He had just a little more sense in him than the king had.

I see the king as somebody wealthy—

had cattle, sheep.

I picture the kings a little bit different.

That king in "Jack and the Varmints" was a pretty good king.

In "Big Jack and Little Jack," the king was pretty mean,

but Jack got even with him.

The King

The king probably got the money from being greedy—
treated people bad and took their money.
Or he could have been a good king, you know, and helped the people.
　　　　These tales trace back to my great-grandpa.
I think these tales come over from England.
You know, they had kings over there.
That's the only thing I can think that the king come from.
But the mountain people—in my opinion—
changed the king and put him in a little old log cabin—
or a big old house with a gold fence about it.
　　　　Jack was kind of a hero to us growing up.
He was kind of a hero like
nowadays kids have a favorite TV show hero, like Superman or Batman.
Back then, Jack was our hero.
Jack was a giant killer, and he caught wild boars.
He caught a lion; he caught a big unicorn.
I could see in my mind that big giant coming at Jack
and then Jack catching that big wild boar.
Sometimes we'd get to thinking we was Jack.
And I wanted to be a giant killer—and catch a lion—
but we never seen a giant back in the mountains.
The biggest thing we seen to a giant was Ray. He was six-foot seven.

　　　　I guess, the new generation coming on,
Jack might be a thing of the past.
I mean, as far as telling,
but I hope to leave some stuff behind—books where they can read.
But I was hoping to make it to 103, so I won't have to worry about that.

JACK AND THE ROBBERS

*N*ow Jack lived wa-a-ay back up in those mountains there with his mama and daddy.

And one day, Jack just got plumb lazy.

He wouldn't do no work.

His mama said,

"Jack, go get the water in from the spring house."

Well, Jack wouldn't do it.

"Jack, go milk the cow before your daddy gets home."

Jack just got lazy and wouldn't do nothing.

Well, that evening, Jack's daddy come out of the field.

He'd been a-working hard.

He looked and seen the work hadn't been done.

He give Jack a hard whipping.

And Jack got mad.

Jack said, "I'm a-running away from home,

and I ain't never coming back here."

Jack got what little clothes he had and put 'em on the end of a stick,

slung 'em over his back, and down the road he went.

Well, Jack walked and walked down that old road till about dinnertime.

He come by this old field.

He looked out in the middle of the field,

and they was a big old steer out there.
That old steer had horns about that long
and had his head hung down, going,

Mrroooo, mrroooo.

Jack looked at that old steer,
and it looked plumb pitiful.
Jack walked out there and said,
"Old steer, what's wrong with you?"

"O-o-oh," said the steer,
"I'm getting so old.
I can't pull the plow no more.
My master don't need me.
He's gonna get rid of me tomorrow
and get a new steer here."

"Well," Jack said,
"that won't do at-all. You better come go with me."
He said, "I'm running away from home."

Down the road Jack and the steer went.
They walked on and on down that old road.
And it wasn't long, they come to another old field.
Had an old fence around it.
Jack looked out in the middle of it.
They was an old donkey out there,
its head hung down, going,

Hee-haw, hee-haw.

The donkey sounded plumb pitiful.

Jack walked up to that old donkey and said,
"You sound plumb awful," he said.
"What's wrong with you?"

"O-o-oh," said the donkey, "I'm getting so old.
My master can't ride on my back, and I can't take him to town.
He ain't got no use for me no more.
He said he's gonna get rid of me tomorrow
and get a new donkey here."

"Well," Jack said,
"you better come go with us."
He said,
"We're running away from home."
So down the road Jack and the steer
and the donkey went.

Well, they walked on
and on and on.

It wasn't long they come by this big old fence.
Jack looked up on top of the fence rail.
There sat this big old cat up there, going,

Meowww, meowww.

Jack looked at that old tomcat a-sitting up there.
He said, "You sound plumb awful." He said,
"What's wrong with you?"

"O-o-oh," said the cat.
"Oh, woe, I'm getting so old.
My master put me in the house last night.
Wanted me to catch a rat.
I caught the rat,
but I'm getting so old
the rat jerked my teeth out of my mouth
and got away from me.
They're gonna get rid of me tomorrow
and get a new tomcat here."

"Well," Jack said, "you better come go with us.
We're running away from home."
Down the road Jack and the steer and the donkey and the cat went.
They walked on and on.
It was getting way up in the evening.
They come by this old barnyard.
Jack looked out in the barnyard.
There sat this old hound dog out there,
looking up in the sky, going,

Bowroo-oo-oo.

Jack said that dog did sound plumb awful.
Jack walked up there and said, "Old dog, what's wrong with you?"
"What's wrong with me?" said the old dog.
"I'm getting so old I can't chase a rabbit.
Can't hardly bark no more.
Ain't got but two good teeth left.
Can't hardly bite nobody.
My master's gonna get rid of me tomorrow
and get a new hound dog here."
"Oh," said Jack,
"that won't do at-all, not at-all."
He said, "Just come on, go with us.
We're running away from home."
Down the road Jack and the steer
and the donkey and the cat and the dog went.
Well, they walked on
and on and on—getting nearly dark.
They come by this red barn.
Jack looked on top on the barn.

On the main top of it sat an old rooster up there.

Its tail feathers gone—it looked plumb pitiful.

It rared back, going,

Cocka-cocka-doodle-doo!

Jack looked at that rooster and said,

"You sound plumb awful. What's wrong with you?"

"O-o-oh," said the rooster. "We got company coming tomorrow,
and they're gonna put me in a chicken pie."

"Oh," said Jack, "That won't do at-all. Gosh, no," he said.

"You better come go with us. We're running away from home."

Down the road Jack and the steer and the donkey and the cat and the dog
and the rooster went.

Well, they walked on and on.

Got in the woods and they got lost.

Gosh, they walked through the woods way up in the night
out there in the middle of nowhere.

And Jack said, "We'd better find a place to spend the night.

No telling what kind of animals are in these woods."

They kept on a-walking.

Finally, the old cat said,

"Look, Jack. I see a light shining off down in the holler yonder."

Jack looked off down in the holler.

There was a little old cabin down there that had a lamp a-burning in the window.

Jack said, "Maybe whoever lives there will let us spend the night with 'em."

Well, Jack and all the animals walked down in that little old holler,
and they come up to the house.

And Jack went up on the porch
and knocked and knocked on the door.

And knocked.

It wasn't nobody at home.

Well, Jack turned the doorknob and the door opened.
Jack went on in the house.
All the animals come in behind him.
    They got in that little old house,
and Jack got to looking around.
And in the corner was a table.
On that table was some old food,
a few pieces of money,
and some old clothes about wore out.
    And Jack said, "Huh-oh."
    The cat said, "What is it?"
    Jack said, "This is the house of the highway robbers."
He said, "If they come back and find us in here,
no telling what they're liable to do to us.
We'd better get out of here."
    The cat said, "Jack, it's too late."
It said, "We'd better hide.
I hear 'em a-coming down the road now."
    Well, the cat jumped in the fireplace and raked ashes over itself.
The dog got behind the chair and hid.
Jack got him a big old stove-wood stick and got behind the door.
The donkey got out against the steps.
The steer got up against the fence up there.
And the rooster flew to the top of the chimney.
    Well, here come seven highway robbers down the road.
And they got up there to the fence where the old steer was hid at,
and they stopped.
One of the robbers said,
"One of you boys go in the house and check around.
See if anybody's been here while we're gone.

44

If it ain't been nobody here," he said,

"build a fire in the fireplace, and we'll come on in."

      Well, that robber went in the house.

He looked around.

Didn't see nobody.

But he looked in the fireplace,

and he seen them two cat eyes a-shining.

He thought they was fire coals.

That robber got him a piece of paper

and got down on his knees.

He stuck that paper in the fireplace in the cat's face—

hwwooo, hwwooo—

blowing, trying to get a fire going.

      That cat got mad, jumped out and went,

Meooowrr!

Scratched the robber in the eyes.

That robber jumped up,
took off a-running.
He got to the chair.
The dog jumped up with them two teeth he had left
and bit a chunk out of the robber's leg.
   Well, that robber made it to the door.
And Jack took that big stove-wood stick,
knocked the robber in the back of the head.
He rolled down the steps and hit the bottom of the steps.
The donkey kicked him real hard,
kicked him up to the fence.
And the steer grabbed him with that long horn
and threwed him way over the fence.
And the rooster was at the top of the chimney, going,

Cockadoodle-doo! Cockadoodle-doo!

   It scared them robbers plumb to death!
They took down the road a-running
as hard as they could run.
The other one took out running behind him.
   "Help me! Help me! I'm dead! I'm dead!
Don't go back to that house."
He said, "It's full of witches, devils, and everything."
He said, "I went to build a fire in the fireplace,
and the witch jumped out and scratched my eyes nearly out.
Got over to a chair,
and a man took a butcher knife and cut a chunk out of my leg."
He said, "I finally got to the door,
and a giant took his big fist,
knocked me down the steps.
And I don't know what it was that kicked me up to the devil.

Devil grabbed his pitchfork and
throwed me way over the fence.
But," he said, "the worst part, the worst part of it all,
there was another man top of the chimney, hollering,
'Throw him up here, boys, when you get done with him.'"

Gosh, it scared them robbers.
They took out of that country and never was seen again.

But Jack and that steer and that donkey and that cat and the dog
and the rooster—
they all got together and they moved in that little old shack down there,
and there they lived happy ever after.

Least-ways that's what Mama said.

*A houseful, a yardful,
but you can't catch a spoonful.*

What is it?
(Smoke)

JACK AND THE VARMINTS

Jack was a young boy,
and he lived back up in the mountains there with his mama.

They was real poor.

And they got up one morning.

Got to looking.

Didn't have nothing to eat hardly at home—

not nothing at-all.

She said, "Jack, son, you're gonna have to go out and find some work.

If you don't, we're gonna starve to death."

Now, Jack, he didn't like to work too good.

Jack didn't want to starve to death neither.

He was getting hungry.

Now, Jack went down the road looking for work.

Well, Jack got down the road a little piece,

and he found an old board that come off an old covered wagon.

Jack picked that board up

and got his old pocketknife out.

Got to whittling on that board.

Jack was going down the road, a-whittling on that board.

Wasn't even looking where he was going.

Before he knowed it, Jack had hewed out a big old round paddle.

Jack got that old paddle,
slinging it this way and that way
a-going down the road.
He come up on a mud hole.
Jack looked and they was a bunch of flies
a-flying around that mud hole.
Well, in a few minutes, all the flies lit in the mud hole.
Now, Jack snook up on that mud hole with that paddle,
and he come down—

Kerwham! —

right in the middle of the mud hole.

He picked the paddle up and looked under it.
He'd killed seven flies.
Now, Jack thought he'd done something big.

Jack went on down the road till he come to the blacksmith's shop.
He went in there and got that man to make him a belt.
Jack put that belt on,
and on the belt, it read,
"Big man Jack killed seven at a whack."

Gosh, Jack was a-feeling big now!
He went down the road with that belt on,
a-feeling as big as he could feel.

It wasn't long, old Jack come by the king's house.
Well, the king was sitting on the porch there in his rocking chair all rared back,
and he seen Jack and he said,
"Howdy-do, son."

Jack looked up and said, "Howdy do, daddy."

Old king said, "Can I help you?"

Jack said, "Yeah, I'm looking for work."

"Well, well, I need a man. I need a man bad,

but I don't believe you're bigger enough for what I need you for.

Come on up here and set down and talk to me a while anyway."

Well, Jack went up on the porch,

and he set down in the old chair beside the king,

and they got to talking.

Directly, old Jack leaned back in his chair,

and the king seen his belt.

And he read it.

"Big man Jack killed seven at a whack."

"Gosh, Jack, does that belt mean what it says it does?"

"Ha!" Jack said, "It sure does, King!"

The king said, "Gosh, you're just the man I've been looking for."

Jack said, "What'd you mean?"

He said, "Across the mountain here, a big wild boar's got loose.

It weighs nearly two thousand pounds.

It's got tusks a-hanging way out,

and people is scared to death of it.

It's a-tearing down fences and barns.

People want me to stop it, me being the king."

He said, "You go back there and get it for me;

I'll give you a thousand dollars."

Jack said, "Gosh, a thousand dollars. I could give it a try.

If I had that kind of money, I wouldn't have to go out and work.

I'd go back home."

Jack said, "All right, King." He said, "I'll give it a try."

Old king went out, saddled his horse up,

and put Jack on behind him.

He rode Jack wa-a-ay across the mountain there where he last seen that wild boar.

The king was so scared of it—what people said.

He got scared, and he knocked Jack off'n the horse,
and the king took off—going back into town he went, just a-getting it.

Jack got up and watched that king ride off, and he said, "Gosh,
if the king's that scared of that wild boar, I'd better not mess with it.
A thousand dollars won't do a dead man no good."
And Jack started home.

Well, Jack got down in the laurel bushes and the thickets,
and he got lost.
He got to beating, thrashing around,
making a lot of racket.
And the old wild boar heared him coming,
making all that racket.
And Jack looked up,
and here come that wild boar down the side of the mountain—
them tusks hanging out this way,
and one hanging out this way,
knocking trees down and rocks over.
Jack seen that thing a-coming.
Boy, he took off a-running.
Here he went
down through the woods.
And here come that wild boar right behind him—

Whippity-cut, whippity-cut, whippity-cut!

Here it come.
Jack was running hard as he could run,
the wild boar right behind him.
And Jack said, "I gotta do something.
If I don't, that thing's gonna catch me and kill me in a minute."

Well, Jack was running,
and he come to the edge of the woods
and looked out there in a little old clearing.
They was a little log cabin out there.
Jack looked.
The top of the cabin had fell in, but the rest of it was still standing.
Well, Jack run hard as he could run.
Got to the door of the log cabin.
The wild boar caught him by the coattail
and jerked a big chunk out of it.

Gosh, Jack shot in the log cabin. The wild boar come in behind him.
They was running around in that cabin, about to tear it down,
and Jack finally cloom up to the top of it and jumped out.
He run around there and pushed the door shut right quick.
Put a rock up against it.
There was that wild boar in that cabin—couldn't get out.
And Jack went on back down to the king's house.

The king was sitting there on the porch, and Jack walked up on the porch.
The king said, "Hey, Jack, did you see that wild boar?"

"Well, no, King, I ain't seen no wild boar."

"Now, Jack, the last ten men I sent up there,
that wild boar nearly killed 'em,
and you didn't even see it?"

Jack said, "No, the only thing I seen
was a little old pig up on the mountain—
a pretty little pig.
I made a pet out of it
and was gonna take it home and give it to Mama.
But looky here—bit my coattail here
and made me mad.

I picked it up by the tail and by the ear and threw it in the log cabin up there.
But you go up there and see if that's what you might want."

Well, the king rode back up there and looked down in the holler
in that log cabin—that big old wild boar in there.

He said, "Gosh, what a man Jack is
to pick up something like that by the tail and by the ear."

The king went back to town.
Got sixty of his mans with Winchester rifles,
and they come back.
Gosh, that wild boar was making so much racket,
nearly tearing the cabin down.
They was scared to get close to it.

And Jack finally got closer enough to the cabin,
poked a gun through the hole,
shot the wild boar between the eyes,
and killed it deader'n a hammer.
It was so big, it took twenty-four wagonloads of meat
to haul it back to the king's house.

Gosh, they got back to the king's house.
The king give Jack his thousand dollars.
Jack stuck it down in his pocket.
Gosh, a thousand dollars. He was rich!

Jack started down the road a-whistling—going home.
He hadn't more than nary got down the road a little piece
and the king hollered,
"Jack, wait a minute!"

. . .

Jack stopped and looked back and said, "What is it, King?"
"Son," the king said, "I just got word in that a big old unicorn's got loose.
It's got one horn in the middle of its head.

It's a-tearing down fences and barns,

and people is scared to death of it.

I gotta have it stopped.

Go back out there and catch it for me and bring it back here,

and I'll give you another thousand dollars."

       Jack said, "Well, bedad, I believe I could give it a try."

       King saddled his horse up, put Jack on behind him.

Brought him wa-a-ay across the mountain where they last seen that unicorn at.

The king knocked Jack off'n the horse,

and, boy, he took off. Back into town he went, just a-getting it.

       Jack got up and watched the king ride off,

and Jack said, "I'm a-going home.

I got a thousand dollars right here in my pocket.

I don't need no more money."

Well, Jack started across the mountain—home.

Jack was walking up the mountain.

He didn't know the unicorn was coming up the other side of the mountain.

Right smack-dab on top of that mountain,

Jack and that unicorn ran into each other.

Jack looked up and there stood that unicorn—that horn stuck out.

He was a-pawing the ground and snorting

Boy, Jack took off a-running as hard as he could run.

Down through the woods he went,

and here come that unicorn behind him—

Whippity-cut, whippity-cut, whippity-cut!

Here it come.

      Jack was running,

dodging this way and that way, running behind trees,

ducking this way and ever' which way.

That unicorn caught up with him.

Stuck its horn about that far into Jack's back.

      Jack said, "I got to do something. If I don't, that thing's gonna kill me.

Jack run and run till he come to a big old tree.

And Jack grabbed that tree

and he swung around it.

The unicorn was going so fast, it couldn't stop. It hit the tree,

and drove its horn plumb through the tree.

      Well, Jack didn't hear it running no more,

and he looked back.

And there was that unicorn hung in the tree,

its horn stuck plumb through the tree.

Jack walked up to it.

Slapped it a little bit.

Seen it couldn't get loose,
and he went on back to the king's house.

      The king was sitting on his porch all rared up in that rocking chair,
leaning back. "Jack, did you see that unicorn?"

      Jack said, "No."

      The king said, "What did you see?"

      Jack said, "I seen a little old calf up on the mountain,
a funny-looking calf.
Didn't have but one horn in the middle of its head.
And I made a pet out of it.
I was gonna take it home and give it to Mama.
But looky, it stuck its horn in my back right here.
Made me mad.
I picked it up by the tail and by the ear and threw it into a tree up there."
He said, "You go up there and see if that's what you might want."

      Well, the king got his mans.
They rode back up on the mountain.
Looked down in the holler.
There was that unicorn, hung in the tree and couldn't get loose.
They was scared of it.
But Jack walked down in the holler and pet the unicorn a little bit.
They seen it couldn't get loose
and couldn't hurt Jack.
They rode down in there.
They got some rope around its neck,
cut the tree down and got it loose.
Took the unicorn back to the king's house.
The old king turned it loose out in the field where it couldn't get out no more
and couldn't bother nobody.
The king give Jack another thousand dollars.

Gosh, Jack had two thousand dollars in his pocket!

He was a rich man.

He went down the road, his hands in his pockets, a-whistling.

He hadn't more than nary got out of sight, and the king said, "Jack, wait a minute!"

. . .

Jack looked back and said, "What is it now, King?"

"I just got word in that a big old lion's got loose.

It's done eat two people.

I got to have it stopped—me being the king.

People is scared to death of it."

He said, "If you'll go back out there and get it for me,

I'll give you another thousand dollars."

Jack said, "Get somebody else to do it. I'm a-going home."

The king said, "Come on, Jack.

You killed seven at a whack.

You got that wild boar, and you caught the unicorn.

You ain't scared of that lion, are you?"

"Huh." Jack said, "I reckon not."

The king saddled his horse up

and put Jack on behind him.

Rode him wa-a-ay across the mountain

where they last seen that big lion.

Gosh, the king'd heared so much about that lion, he was scared of it.

He knocked Jack off'n that horse and that king took off.

Boy, he was gone.

Jack got up and watched that king ride off.

He said, "Huh, I ain't gonna mess with no lion.

I got two thousand dollars in my pocket,

and I'm a-going home.

He said, "As a matter of fact, I'm gonna stay on this little-bitty road here
to take me home,
and I ain't getting lost.
I ain't getting in the woods.
    Jack started down that little bitty road there going home,
He got down the road a little piece,
and he come around a bend in the road.
And right smack-dab in the middle of that road sat that old lion,
its teeth a-hanging out.

Grrrrrr!

Gosh, they said it roared so loud, it shook the trees out of the ground.
The king heared it plumb in town.
    The king said, "Gosh, Jack's a goner now."
    It scared poor Jack so bad,
that big lion growling like that instead of running.
Jack cloom up a tree.
They say he cloom plumb up to the top of it.
    And here come that lion up the road
a-smelling and a-sniffing.
That lion got under that tree—
and them teeth about that long a-hanging out.
Looked up in that tree and seen Jack.
Got to gnawing on the tree—like a ax.
Nearly had it cut down.
Jack was up there, and his knees was knocking—scared to death.
Directly that old lion got tired and sleepy
and dropped off and went to sleep,
    And Jack said, "I'm a-getting out of here."
    Jack put his foot down,
put it on an old brittle limb, and it broke.

So Jack fell out of the top of the tree
and fell on top of the lion's back.

    That lion jumped up from its sleep,
scared to death
and Jack on it's back.

Raaar, raaar!

Tried to bite him.
Tried to claw him.
And that lion run through the bushes,
trying to get Jack off its back.
And Jack was hanging onto that lion for dear life, scared to death—
hanging onto its mane.
That lion took off a-running.
Right into town that lion went.

  That king was sitting on the porch rared back in that rocking chair,
and he seen Jack a-coming on the lion's back and said,
"Gosh, what a man Jack is
to ride a lion like that."
He got his old hog rifle.
First shot he missed and shot Jack's hat off.
Jack was getting scared to death
on that lion's back and the king shooting his hat off.

  Directly, the old lion come back around the king's house again.
The king took better aim,
shot the lion between the eyes,
and killed it deader'n a hammer.
It fell over in the street.
The king walked over there.
Jack was getting up, dusting himself off.

  The king got over there, and Jack said, "Looky here, King.
I'm mad. I'm good and mad."

  The king said, "Mad? What you mad about?
I shot that lion."

Jack said, "That's what I'm mad about."
He said, "I caught that lion up on the mountain.
I was training it for you a ridy horse.
And you up and shot it
and wasted my time.
That makes me mad."
He said, "You'd look big,
being the king, riding that thing up through town."

　　And the king felt sorry for Jack.
Give him an extra thousand dollars.
And old Jack went on home with four thousand dollars in his pocket.

　　Last time I was down there to see that lazy rascal,
him and his mama was doing real good,
and Jack still ain't done a good day's work.

This is one of my favorite tales.

BIG JACK AND LITTLE JACK

Big Jack and Little Jack was out roaming the country
over the mountains, looking for work.

Gosh, back in them times, nobody didn't have no money to pay nobody.

They'd been gone from home for three or four months.

They hadn't made one dime—

not one thin dime.

  And one day,

Big Jack and Little Jack was walking through the woods,

and they come to the forks of the road there.

Big Jack said, "Little Jack, you take the left-hand fork of the road,

and I'll take the right-hand fork of the road.

And one of us might be able to find a job."

  Well, Little Jack headed down the left-hand fork of the road,

and Big Jack, he started walking down the right-hand fork of the road.

Big Jack, he walked and walked. Nearly three days went by.

He was walking through the woods,

and he come to the biggest house he'd ever seen in his life

out there in the middle of nowhere.

Big Jack said, "Gosh, I wonder who could live in a place like this?"

  Big Jack walked up on the porch and knocked on the door.

Old man opened the door and said, "Can I help you, son?"

"Yeah," said Big Jack. "I'm looking for work."

He said, "Who are you?"

"Who am I?"

He said, "Son, I'm the king.

I'm the king of this whole country here."

He said, "I can give you a job tending to a hundred head of sheep

and pay you fifty cent a day."

"Well," said Big Jack, "that sounds good to me."

He said, "When can I start to work?"

The king said, "Wait a minute, wait a minute, Big Jack."

He said, "I got a rule made here."

Big Jack said, "What kind of rule?"

The king said, "Well, if I make you mad,

I get to knock you down and cut three strops out of your back

and won't have to pay you."

"Well," said Big Jack, "that's all right with me.

I ain't never been mad at nobody in my life anyway."

The king said, "Well, good. You can go to work in the morning."

He said, "Go on to bed."

He sent Big Jack to bed.

Didn't give him no supper, not one bite.

He got Big Jack up at six o'clock in the morning.

Sent him up on the mountain with a hundred head of sheep to watch all day.

He didn't give him no breakfast.

Well, come dinnertime, Big Jack got hungry,

and he found a few berries, and he picked 'em and eat 'em.

About five o'clock come. Big Jack come in with the sheep.

The king met him at the gate.

He counted his sheep.

"Ninety-eight, ninety-nine, one hundred.

Good job, Big Jack! Go on to bed."

He sent Big Jack back to bed with no supper.

Well, he got Big Jack up at six o'clock in the morning again.
Sent him up on the mountain with a hundred head of sheep to watch all day—
not one bite of breakfast. Not nothing.

Come dinnertime, Big Jack begin to get hungry.
He found a few berries
and picked 'em and eat 'em. It wasn't much left to eat.

And that evening, he come in with the sheep about five o'clock.
The king met him at the gate and counted his sheep.
"Ninety-eight, ninety-nine, one hundred.
Good job, Big Jack! Go on the bed."

Big Jack said, "Wait a minute, King. Ain't you gonna feed me?"

The king said, "No, I hired you to work, not to eat.
You ain't mad, are you?"

"Mad? Yeah, I'm good and mad!
You shouldn't treat a man like that—
work him hard all day and won't feed him.
That's enough to make a man mad."
And he come after the king with his fists.
He remembered the rule the king made.

The king knocked him down,
cut three strops out of his back,
and didn't pay him a dime—
not nothing.

Big Jack went hobbling down the road.

The next morning, Big Jack met up with Little Jack.
Little Jack said, "Go-o-osh, what's wrong with you, Big Jack?"

"O-o-oh, Little Jack, if you're looking for work,
don't go up there to that king's house.

That's the meanest man that ever lived.
Work you all day; won't feed you. Get mad at you.
Cut three strops out of your back and won't pay you."
      "Well," said Little Jack,
"you go on down there and see the doctor,
and I'll go up there and take care of the king."
      And Big Jack went hobbling down the road to the doctor.
      Little Jack, he went on up the road there.
And he walked and he walked till he come to the king's house.
He walked up on the porch.
Little Jack knocked on the door.
      The king come out.
He said, "Well, howdy."
      "Howdy," said Little Jack.
      The king said, "Can I help you?"
      "Yeah," said Little Jack. "I'm looking for work."
      "Well, I need a man
 to tend to a hundred head of sheep and pay him fifty cent a day."
      "Well," said Little Jack, "that sounds good to me."
He said, "When can I go to work?"
      "Wait a minute, Little Jack," the king said.
"I got a rule made here."
      Little Jack said, "What kind of rule?"
      The king said, "If I make you mad,
I get to knock you down and cut three strops out of your back
and won't have to pay you."
      "Well," said Little Jack, "That's all right with me."
He said, "I ain't never been mad at nobody in my life anyway."
Little Jack said, "That ought to go two ways, old King."
      The king said, "What do you mean?"

Little Jack said, "If I can make you mad before you make me mad,"
he said, "I'll knock you down, cut three strops out of your back,
and you pay me double."

"Yeah," said the king. "We can make the deal.
Go on to bed."
He sent Little Jack to bed. Didn't give him no supper.

He got Little Jack up at six o'clock in the morning.
Sent him up on the mountain with a hundred head of sheep to watch all day.
Didn't give him no breakfast.

Well, dinnertime come around,
and Little Jack got hungry.
He picked a stick up off the ground,
knocked the biggest sheep on the head,
and killed it deader'n a hammer.
He skinned it out and cooked it
and eat it for his dinner.

That evening about five o'clock, he come in.
The king met him at the gate and counted his sheep.
Ninety-eight, ninety-nine. Ninety-nine!
Wait a minute, Little Jack! Wait a minute!
One of my sheep's gone."

"Well," said Little Jack, "it ought to be gone. You wouldn't feed me.
I had to knock it in the head and eat it for dinner."
He said, "You ain't mad, are you?"

"Mad! No, no, no, no, son. I ain't mad at-all.
But," he said, "you ain't tending no more of my sheep.
Ninety-nine more days, I wouldn't have a sheep left."
He said, "How are you at plowing?"

"Oh," said Little Jack, "back where I come from,
they said I was the best plow hand that ever lived."

The king said, "Well, good.
I'm gonna put you down there plowing the field."

Well, the king went to the barn.
He got two of the finest horses—big matching pair.
Put silver bridles on 'em, silver harnesses.
And he took 'em down there and hooked 'em up to a plow
and told Little Jack to go to work.

Well, Little Jack was plowing,
doing pretty good till the king got out of sight.
Little Jack just throwed the plow down and laid under a shade tree.
Little Jack was laying under that shade tree, nearly asleep,
and he heared a racket.
And he looked, and coming down the road going into town
was an old man riding on a little old donkey—going down the road.

Little Jack hollered to him, "Hey, mister."

That old man stopped and looked back and said, "What do you want?"

Little Jack said, "What'd I want?
What'd you take for that little old donkey you're riding?"
That man said, "Son,
you shouldn't make fun of me and my little old donkey—
you got two big, fine horses like that."
Little Jack said, "I wasn't making fun of you and that donkey."
He said, "I'd love to have that donkey.
I'll trade you one of these horses even for it."
That man said, "You'd trade your fine horse even for my little old donkey
and it about dead?"
Jack said, "I'll swap even."
Well, he made the swap,
and that evening, the king come down there to check on Little Jack.
There he was plowing the field
with the big horse hooked to the plow and a little donkey beside of it.
The king hollered, "Wait a minute, Little Jack! Wait a minute!"
Little Jack stopped and said, "What is it now, King?"
"What is it now?"
He said, "Where's my horse at?"
"O-o-oh," said Little Jack, "your horse." He said,
"King, I seen that man riding that little old donkey,
and that thing so pretty.
You being the king, I figured you'd want it,
and I traded your horse even for it.
You ain't mad are you?"
"Mad, mad, mad? No, no, no, son, I ain't mad at-all. No, I ain't mad,
but you ain't plowing no more.
How are you at picking apples?"
"O-o-oh, gosh," said Little Jack,
"I'm the best apple picker that ever lived."

The king said, "Well, good."
He took Jack up to the apple orchard
and told him to go to work,
and the king left.

The king got out of sight,
and Little Jack went down to the woodshed,
got him a ax,
and went back up there and cut four of the biggest apple trees down
and laid 'em on the ground.

That evening, the king came up there to check on Little Jack.
There was four of his apple trees chopped down
and Little Jack picking apples off of them.

The king said, "Wait a minute, Little Jack!"

Little Jack said, "What is it now, King?"

He said, "What did you cut my apple trees down like that for?"

Little Jack said, "They're easier to pick like that."

The king said, "Here, I'll show you how to pick a apple."
He got a ladder and set it in the apple tree,
and the king cloom up the ladder.

He got to the bottom limb of the apple tree.
Little Jack run out there and jerked the ladder out from the king.
The king grabbed the apple limb that was hanging there.

"Get me down from here, Little Jack.
What'd you do that for?"

Little Jack said, "Why don't you feed me?
A man'd get mighty hungry working for you."

The king said, "You go down to the house,
and tell my wife to cook you some supper and be quick about it."

Little Jack run down to the house and went in the kitchen.
Told the king's wife, "The king sent me down here to kiss you."

"Kiss me!"

She said, "You dirty little thing, I ain't kissing you!"

Little Jack went back up on the porch and hollered,

"Hey, king, she won't do it."

The king hollered back, "She better do it!

I'm getting tired of hanging here.

I'm getting mad."

She heard the king holler,

and she grabbed Little Jack and gave him a big old kiss.

Little Jack went back up to the apple tree and set the ladder up.

The king cloom down the ladder.

Little Jack cloom back up the ladder and got in the apple tree

picking apples.

The king went to the house.

When he got to the house, his wife jumped all over him.

She said, "What'd you send that dirty little boy down here to kiss me for?"

The king said, "Gosh, I didn't send him down here to kiss you.

You didn't kiss him did you?"

She said, "I sure did."

Boy, the king was roaring mad.

He went back up through there and he got up to the apple tree,

and he said, "Little Jack, did you kiss my wife?"

Little Jack said, "Yeah, I kissed her.

You ain't mad are you?"

"Mad?

Son, I'm good and mad. Wait till I get a-hold of you."

Little Jack just jumped out of the apple tree

and landed on the king's back,

knocked him down, cut three strops out of his back.

Made the king pay him double.

And the king remembered the rule he'd made.
Wasn't nothing he could do about it.

      Little Jack went on back down the road.
He met up with Big Jack.
He give him half that money he got from the king,
and he give him three strops cut out of the king's back.
And they say to this day,
Big Jack is the only person living, walking around,
with a new pair of shoestrings made out of the king's hide.

*People say when the apple trees bear
hard—limbs hanging to the ground—
you can look for a bad winter.
Apples and hickory nuts too.*

JACK AND THE DEVIL

*J*ack went out one day,
 and he met up with the devil.
The old devil and Jack got to talking,
and the devil said, "Jack,
let's me and you go in together and do something."

Jack said, "What do you want to do?"

Devil said, "I don't know."

Jack said, "Well, let's raise some 'taters."

That devil said, "That sounds good to me. How would we divide 'em?"

Jack said, "Well, I'll just take what grows under the ground,
and you can have what grows on top of the ground."

Devil shook his hand and said,
"You got a deal."

Well, it come harvesting time.
Jack went out there and dug all them pretty 'taters out from under the ground—
big old round 'taters,
a paper sack full of 'em.
Devil, all he got was the tops.
Jack took his pretty 'taters to a little old store and sold them.
The old devil took his 'tater tops to the store,
and he found out they wasn't worth nothing.

Boy, the devil got mad, and he come back.
He said, "Jack, let's raise something else together."

Jack said, "How 'bout corn?"

"Yeah, Jack. That sounds pretty good to me.
But," the devil said,
"this time, you take what grows on top of the ground
and let me have what grows under the ground."

Jack said, "You got a deal."

Well, it come time to harvest that corn.
Jack got all them roasting ears out of the top of that corn,
and all the devil got was a bunch of corn roots you pull out of the ground.
He ended up with nothing again.
Boy, he was getting madder and madder.
He said, "Jack,
let's do something else."

Jack said, "Let's raise some hogs."

Devil said, "Well, I can't go wrong with that.
Let's give it a try."

They raised two hundred hogs.
Well, the hogs got bigger enough to divide.
Jack and the devil was going down to the hog pen one morning to divide them.
And Jack had put him a fence on the left-hand side of the hog pen,
and the devil got a fence on the right-hand side.
Well, Jack cut a hole in his little fence to the devil's fence
and put corn out there in his fence.
Every time the devil'd pick up a hog and put it in his side,
it'd run over to the fence
and run out there where all Jack's hogs was eating that corn.

They got done dividing them two hundred hogs.
Devil looked over, and he didn't have a one in his fence.

Looked over in Jack's side,

and there was all them big hogs out there.

Devil said, "Which ones is mine?"

Jack said, "I don't know,

but I twisted all mine's tails before I threw them in my side of the fence."

Devil looked over,

and all two hundred hogs had twisted tails. He couldn't tell which ones was his,

so he ended up with nothing again.

Old devil never could get the best of Jack.

*Mama used to say,
"If you can tell me how many little
pigs I have in this sack, I'll give you
both of them."*

THE CAT AND THE MOUSE

*N*ow, Jack and his two brothers, Tom and Will,
      lived back up there in the mountains with their mama and daddy.
And their daddy had, oh, about a forty-acre farm.

He was getting pretty old.

He was trying to decide which boy to give the farm to.

He called the three boys there—Jack and Tom and Will.

He said, "Boys,
in the evening time," he said, "I'm going to give you'uns a hundred dollars apiece.

I want you'uns to leave home
and not come back till one year's up.

And the one that done best with that hundred dollars I give him,
I'm gonna give him this farm."

Well, he give Jack a hundred dollars
and Tom a hundred and Will a hundred.

He said, "You'uns leave out tomorrow real early.

Come back in one year."

Well, that morning,
Tom and Will got up before Jack got up and went out down the road and hid—
hid in the bushes.

It wasn't long, here come Jack down the road a-whistling,
that hundred dollars in his pocket, hands in his back pocket.

Tom and Will jumped out of the bushes,
and they beat Jack up,
throwed him into the mud hole,
and took his hundred dollars away from him.

Well, it wasn't long, Jack got up out of the mud hole,
beat about half to death and his hundred dollars gone.
He said, "I can't go home till a year's up."
He said, "I'm just gonna have to do the best I can do."

Tom and Will had done took his hundred dollars
and gone down the road with it.
Poor Jack went walking down the road.
He'd been walking—gosh, it was nearly a month—
finding what he could eat in the bushes—
huckleberries or strawberries.
Poor old Jack was about to give up.

He walked one day,
and he come to a little old forks of the road down there.
Jack said, "Which way should I go—
to the left or to the right?"
He said, "I know what I'll do."
He said, "I'll throw my hat off—throw it up in the air.
When it lands,
I'll go whichever way the hat bill's pointing."
Jack took off his hat, throwed it up in the air.
It come on the ground,
and his bill pointed straight on.

Jack went through the woods,
and there was a little wagon road down through there.
Jack said, "Well, that's the way my bill told me to go.
That's the way I'm a-going, bedad."

Jack headed down that old wagon road.

He walked and walked.

About three or four days went by,

and he come to a big old house out there in the middle of the woods,

the middle of nowhere.

Gosh, old barn and fence about to fall down.

It'd growed up around it.

It was the awfullest looking place he'd ever seen.

Jack said, "Well, I know nobody can't live here."

Well, he went up on the porch

and knocked on the door anyway.

      Knocked on the door, and something said, "Come in."

      And Jack opened the door

and looked around.

Jack said, "Who said that?"

      It said, "Me."

      He looked down and there was a cat.

Jack said, "I done come to a country where cats can talk."

About that time a mouse run across the floor in front of the cat.

      That cat said, "No, no, no." It said,

"Me and my sister lived here,

and this mean old witch come here.

She witched my sister into a mouse,

and once you're into a mouse," it said,

"you can't come back. You have to stay a mouse.

And she got me witched into a cat.

And tonight she's gonna witch me into a mouse,"

it said, "and I'll stay a mouse the rest of my life,

like my sister going there."

And there went the mouse back across the floor.

Jack said, "Is there anything I can do to help you?"

The cat said, "Yeah."

It said, "Tonight that witch is gonna send all kind of animals here,
like bears, tigers, lions—
all kind of animals."

It said, "If you can keep 'em out of the house—
don't let one of them in the house, not one of 'em—
it'd help me."

Well, Jack went out to the woodshed,
got the old pole ax.

Got him a bi-i-ig old long stick
and hewed a big old long bat out of it.

And that evening, it begin to get dark,
and Jack got up on the porch of the house
with that big old bat in his hand.

And sure enough, it got dark, and here come lions, tigers, bears—
all kind of big animals.

Jack beat and swarfed, and beat and knocked, beat and knocked.

He knowed he'd killed a thousand of 'em—all night long.

He was given out in the morning.

Daylight come, and he looked out in the yard,
and it wasn't nothing out there.

Jack went in the house and looked.

That cat was kinda looking like a woman a little bit.

It had one woman's hand and still a cat's paw.

And it had a woman's ear,
and it was kinda looking like a woman.

It said, "Now, Jack, tonight that witch's gonna send all kind of animals here
like squirrels, rabbits, possums, raccoons—
small animals.

Don't let none of them in the house,
whatever you do.
If you do, I'll be turned back into a cat and into a mouse,
and that's what I'll stay."

Well, it got nearly dark, and Jack got up on the porch with that bat again,
and sure enough,
here come possums, rats, rabbits—everything—
coming up through there trying to get into the house.
Jack was beating and knocking,
beating and knocking all night long.
And, man, he was sweating.
He was gived out.
Jack said he knowed he killed two thousand of 'em.
He just knowed it.
    Morning come. Looked out in the yard,
and it wasn't nothing.

Well, gosh, he walked back in the house,

and that cat begin to look like a pretty good-looking woman.

He said it had a woman's face kinda,

and it had one cat's ear yet on,

a cat's paw and a few whiskers.

It said, "Now, Jack,

tonight that witch's gonna send all kind of insects

like mosquitoes, flies, bees, hornets, wasps—all kind of stuff.

And whatever you do, don't let none of them into the house."

Well, Jack went out,

found a big board that come off a wagon.

Hewed himself a big old round paddle—

a big one.

And sure enough, it got dark,

and Jack was up on the porch there at the door.

Here come mosquitoes, flies, hornets, all kinds of bees.

Jack beat and swarfed, beat and knocked and swarfed all night long.

He said he knowed he'd killed ten thousand of the insects.

Got up in the morning,

looked out in the yard and it wasn't nothing, not nothing.

Jack went in the house,

and, he said, gosh, there stood a good-looking woman,

except she had a few whiskers across here.

She said, "Now, Jack, tonight the old witch is gonna come herself.

And whatever you do,

don't let her help you or touch nothing of yours.

If you do, she'll witch you into a cat and me into a cat and then into a mouse

like my sister going there," and there went the mouse back across the floor.

"We'll stay a mouse the rest of our life.

Don't let her do nothing for you."

Well, it got dark, and Jack built up a fire in the fireplace
and put him a frying pan there.
Put him some fatback in it.
He sit down there and took his shoes off,
and his socks was full of holes.
That woman went and got him a big old darning needle
and threaded it up.
Jack was in there sewing his socks up.

In a few minutes, the door flew open.

"Heh, heh, heh, heh."

In come an old woman.

Jack said she looked like she was a hundred years old
and she had a long nose.
Jack said she wasn't nothing but bones hardly.
He knowed it was a witch, the way she looked.

Looked over at Jack.
"Lord a'mercy, boy.
I ain't never seen a man sew his own socks up. Let me do that for you."

Jack said, "No, no, I don't want you to do nothing for me!
Stay away from me!"

And the old witch went over to the fireplace and said,
"Your meat's a-burning. Let me turn it over."
She reached in there and started to turn that meat over.
There was a fire hook a-layin there,
and Jack grabbed that fire hook and stuck it in the witch's back.
He threw her in that fire, and he held her there.
She popped and cracked, and blue smoke come up out of that chimney.
Burnt that witch plumb up.

Next morning, Jack looked and there stood that woman,
the prettiest woman he'd ever seen in his life.

She said, "Jack, you saved my life.
Ain't nothing you can do for my sister, going there—
that poor mouse going across the floor.
But," she said, "I'm going to give you this place."
        And Jack went outside and looked,
and that turned into a beautiful place.
Go-o-osh a-mighty—
big beautiful house, barn.
There was big old pretty horses, and cattle running around,
big old carriages and a wagon.
        He went back in.
Jack said, "It's a pretty place, but I don't want it unless you come with it."
        She said, "Jack, you mean that?"
        They went out and got married.
Come back home, and Jack stayed there on that farm,
running it.
Gosh, he was rich, wealthy—all those cattle and horses.
        It wasn't long, Jack told his wife,
"A year's up tomorrow. I need to go home."
He said, "Mama and Daddy give us a hundred dollars apiece.
And Tom and Will beat me up, took my hundred dollars.
I'm going home and show 'em how I made it."
        Well,
the next morning, her and Jack went out
and harnessed up the two biggest, prettiest horses he had.
Hooked them up to a big old carriage.
Jack put his big suit on, his old hat,
scissor-tailed coat, and that big necktie.
Gosh, his wife got prettied up and got in the buggy beside of him.
Went back to Jack's house.

And Tom and Will, they'd got married and come back home.
He said their clothes was still wore out.
Well, they'd come back in the same clothes they had on, but they'd got married.
And their wives' clothes was wore out.
And Jack come up through there riding in that big buggy with his wife.
Will hollered, "Honey, get under the bed. Hide. Hide!
There come some rich people up the road."
His wife got under the bed.
Tom told his wife, he said, "You hide too. Don't let them see you."
He said, "You're dirty too."
And she run and got under the floor.
Jack come riding up there in that buggy, and his mama looked out.
"That ain't a rich fellow. That's my boy Jack. I'd know Jack-a-boy anywhere.
Gosh, he's done got rich. What a pretty woman he got."
Jack rode up there in that buggy.
His daddy and mama come out.
And Jack said, "Tom and Will come home?"
"Yeah, they come home wearing the same clothes they left with."
Jack said, "Well, Daddy, they beat me up and took my money."
He said, "Where're their wives at?"
Jack's daddy said, "Well, Tom's wife went under the floor,
and Will's wife went under the bed." He said, "They're too dirty to come out."
Jack said, "Well, Daddy, you go ahead and give Tom and Will this place.
I'm gonna take you and Mama with me and take care of you.
You and Mama's getting old,
and I'm gonna take care of you'uns the rest of my life.
I ain't giving Tom and Will a dime, the way they treated me."
He got his mama and daddy in that buggy
and took 'em back home.
And he said they put four rocking chairs on the porch of that house.

The last time I was down by there,
Jack and his wife and his mama and daddy—all four of 'em—
was sitting in a rocking chair,
all rared back, taking it easy.
Living a good life.

Mama used to say,
Kitty, kitty, kitty, come over to my house.
Kitty, kitty, kitty, gotta catch me a mouse.

It has a tongue.
You can lead it to water,
but it won't drink.

What is it?
    (A wagon)

Sheepskin

*T*his story is about Jack and his daddy.

They lived back up in the mountains there in a little log cabin.

They was fine builders.

They built houses and cabins for people.

One day, Jack was getting up pretty old,

and Jack's daddy gave him a sheepskin.

His daddy said, "Jack,

I want you to take this sheepskin into town and sell it—

and bring the money back and bring the sheepskin back."

And the next morning, Jack got that old sheepskin.

Went into town, dragging it behind him.

And he got in town, and everybody wanted to buy the sheepskin,

but they didn't want to pay him for it and give it back to him.

Jack come home that evening.

He was about gived out.

He said, "Daddy, I can't find nobody in the town

that'd buy a sheepskin

and pay me for it and give it back to me."

His daddy said, "Son, you go back tomorrow and try again."

The next morning, here went Jack down the road,

dragging that old sheepskin.

Went into town.
Everybody he'd meet—
"You want to buy a sheepskin?"

        "Yeah, we'll buy it."

        "Well, I want the money and I want the sheepskin back."

        They thought he was crazy,
and they said, "Can't do that."

        And Jack come back home that evening and said,
"Daddy, I just can't find nobody wants to buy this sheepskin,
give me the money, and give me the sheepskin back."

        His Daddy said, "Son, go try one more time."

        The next morning, Jack went into town,
dragging that old sheepskin with him.
Everybody he asked said, "Yeah, we'll buy the sheepskin,
but we ain't giving it back to you."

        Well, Jack started home.
He was out of heart, about to give up,
and he come to an old bridge.
He sat down on the bridge there,
looking awful sad.

        In a few minutes, he heard somebody holler,
"You're looking awful sad. What's wrong with you?"

        Looked off the bridge.
There at the creek was a young woman
down there washing her clothes.

        And Jack told her,
"Daddy wanted me to sell the sheepskin,
get the money, and bring the sheepskin back too;
and I can't do it."

        She said, "Bring it down here."

Well, Jack took that sheepskin down there,
and that woman washed it real good.
And she cut the wool off the sheepskin,
and give Jack the sheepskin back
and paid him for the wool.
So he got the money and the sheepskin back.

He went home and said, "Daddy, Daddy,
I sold the sheepskin, got it back, and got the money for it too."
He told his daddy what happened.

His daddy said, "Well, son,
that woman seems like she might make you a good wife."
He said, "Go back and invite her to supper over here."

Jack went over,
and she said, "Yeah, I'll be over to eat with you."

Well, that woman come over that evening.
They were sitting there eating supper,
and her and Jack got to talking.
Finally, got to courting.

It wasn't long, her and Jack got married.
Well, they was living with his daddy.

The king got word that Jack and his daddy was good builders.
This old king sent word to Jack and his daddy
to come and build him a castle.
He said, "I want the finest castle built,
like no other king had a castle built like that."

So Jack and his daddy got what tools they had together
and started down the road to the king's place.

They got down the road a little piece, and his daddy said,
"Jack, make this road shorter for me."

Jack said, "I don't know what you're talking about."

His daddy said, "Well, just go on back home. I don't need you."

Jack went back home, his head hung down,

and his wife said, "What's wrong?"

"Well, Daddy said to make the road shorter for him,

and I didn't know what he was talking about."

She said, "You silly thing! Tell him a tale.

That'd make the road shorter."

Jack run and caught up with his daddy.

Started telling him a tale.

When he got done with the tale, they was plumb at the king's house.

It'd made the road shorter.

Well, when they got to the king's house,

they started into building the king a castle.

They worked and worked for months

building the king that castle.

When they got done, it was the prettiest castle ever built in the world.

Jack and his daddy was going home the next day.
They was staying in a room there,
and this man come to 'em.
He worked for the king.

The man said, "The king ain't gonna let you'uns go home.
He's gonna kill you."

Jack's daddy said, "Why?"

"Well, he don't want you to go out
and build another castle this pretty for any other king.
He's gonna kill you'uns tomorrow
so you can't do it."

So the next morning,
the king come in the room where Jack and his daddy was.
The king said, "Is the castle finished?"

Jack's daddy said, "We've got one more thing we need to do,
but we left the special tool at home we need to do it with."
He said, "I'll send Jack after it."

The king said, "No, no, no, I'll send my son after it."
And the king didn't have but one son.

The king's son said, "What do you need?"

Jack's daddy said,
"Well, just tell Jack's wife we need the straight and the narrow tool."

The king's son said, "The straight and the narrow?"

Jack's daddy said, "Yeah, but she'll know what you're talking about."
The king's son, the only one he had,
went to Jack's house and knocked on the door.
And Jack's wife opened the door.

He said, "I'm the king's son,
and the king sent me after a special tool Jack and his daddy need,
called 'the straight and the narrow.'"

Jack's wife knowed right then
that was the word Jack and his daddy used when they was in danger.
She knowed they was in trouble.

She said, "It's over there in that chest."
And she opened that chest up and said, "I can't reach it."
She said, "You're gonna have to reach down there and get it for me."

The king's son went over there to reach down into the chest.
She grabbed him, throwed him in the chest,
and shut him up and locked him up in there.
She sent word back to the king,
"If anything happens to Jack and his daddy,
you'll never see your son again."

The only son the king had—
boy, the king got scared and turned Jack and his daddy loose.
Jack and his daddy come home,
and Jack's wife turned the king's son loose,
let him go back home.

Jack and his daddy was so happy that Jack's wife saved their life.
So Jack and his daddy built her the finest castle that ever was built.
It was bigger and better and prettier than the one they built for the king.
Prettiest castle in the whole world.

And as far as I know,
Jack and his wife and his daddy are still living in it.

If you're gonna tell it, tell it big.

JACK AND THE KING'S MOUNTAIN

*T*his old king lived back there in the mountains,
  and, gosh, he had this real pretty girl.
    And all the boys around there got to courting that girl.
Gosh, they come down out of the mountain.
Some of 'em, their britches had patches on them.
Some of 'em was barefooted.
You know, back then, poor people didn't have nothing.
Lucky to have a pair of britches,
and them patched, I guess.
And they'd come down courting that girl.
    That king said, "Gosh, this won't do at-all—
not none of these boys."
He finally got tired of 'em all coming,
and he told 'em when they come, he said,
"I'm gonna ask you a question.
If you can answer it," he said, "you can marry my girl.
If you can't, you'll just have to stay here and work for me for a year—
work on the farm,
milk cows,
and build fences,
and anything I want you to do."

Them boys said, "Yeah, yeah."

The king would ask 'em, he said,

"Well, they's a mountain behind the house here.

How many baskets of dirt would it take to move it?"

Them boys took a guess,

and he'd say, "No, you're wrong."

And he'd keep 'em there to work.

It wasn't long, they wasn't no boys left in the neighborhood hardly

but Jack and Tom and Will.

And, gosh, they was poor.

Will had a pair of shoes.

I don't think Tom even had a pair.

Well, Will seen that girl,

and he went down there to court her.

And the king said,

"I'm gonna have to ask you a question.

If you can answer it," he said, "you can marry her,

but if you can't," he said, "you'll have to stay and work for me."

Will said, "That's all right with me."

The king said, "See that mountain back here?"

And Will said, "Yeah."

"How many baskets of dirt would it take to move it?"

Will said, "Oh, about a thousand baskets."

The king said, "No, no.

You're wrong."

He just kept Will there,

put him to work with the rest of the boys.

Back at home, that left Tom and Jack.

And Tom seen that king's girl out at the edge of the meadow one day

picking flowers.

And he decided he'd go.

He'd fell in love with her.

And Tom went down there to the king's house barefooted,

and his old britches patched up,

and knocked on the door.

And the king come out, and he said,

"Can I help you, son?"

Tom said, "Yeah,

I come down here to court your girl."

That king looked at him, up and down

and said, "Gaw, court my girl!"

He said, "I'm gonna ask you a question.

If you can answer it, you can marry her.

But if you can't," he said, "you have to go to work with the rest of the boys."

Tom said, "Well, that's all right with me."

The king said, "See that mountain back here?"

Tom looked at it and said, "Yeah."

The king said, "How many baskets of dirt would it take

to move that mountain?"

Tom said, "Ah, about twenty-five hundred."

The king said, "No, no, you're wrong,"

and he kept Tom there and put him to work for him.

That left the only boy—about—in the neighborhood was Jack.

Jack stayed there and helped his mama.

One day, Jack was out picking up wood, and he seen that girl.

She was out at the edge of the woods picking huckleberries or something.

And Jack seen her. Gosh, he just fell in love with her—she was so pretty.

Jack wanted to go on down to the king's house,

and Jack's mama begged him not to go.

She said, "Jack, don't go.

Tom and Will done gone for a year.
Won't be nobody around here to help."

     Jack said, "I gotta go, Mama.
Gosh," he said, "that girl's pretty."

     And Jack headed down to the king's house.
Went up and knocked on the door, and the old king come out,
and there stood Jack
in his old clothes and his old hat flopped down.

     The king said, "Can I help you son?"

     Jack said, "Yeah. I come down here to court your girl."

     "Huh!" the king said, "Court my girl!"
He said, "To court my girl—or to marry her—
I'm gonna ask you a question.
If you answer it,"
he said, "you can marry the girl.
but if you can't,
you're gonna have to stay and work for me a year."

     Jack said, "Well, if I can answer the question, I'll marry her,
but will you let all the boys back loose and let 'em go home?
The mamas and daddies ain't got nobody to help 'em.

     The king said, "Yeah, we'll make the deal."
He said, "See that mountain back there?"

     Jack looked at it and said, "Yeah."

     The king said, "How many baskets of dirt would it take to move it?"

     Jack stepped back and took his old hat off
and scratched his head and looked at the mountain again.
"Well, King,
it wouldn't take but one basket if the basket was bigger enough."

     The king, he thought a minute and scratched his old head and said,
"You know, you're right. You answered that right"

He said, "You're a pretty smart boy.
I'd be glad to have you marry my girl."

So Jack and the king's girl got married.
And Jack stayed down around there,
and the king give him a little place of land to live on,
built 'em a little old cabin on it.
And he turned all the boys loose.
Tom and Will and all of them went back home.

And last time I was down through there to see that rascal,
Jack and the king's girl was doing good.
Tom and Will was still home helping their mama—
working around the house.

Other Traditional Tales

As Orville grew up, children listened to tales around the woodstove on cold nights and on the porch as summer's evening shadows wrapped the mountains. His mother, Sarah Harmon Hicks, knew she could keep her children nearby if she told them stories. She often entertained the children with tales as they worked in the garden or hunted herbs in the woods. She told tales as they sat on the porch in the evenings to snap beans or to tie galax bunches for sale to the floral market.

Some of these folktales told by Orville's mother bear messages about good and evil, some are reminders or warnings, and some are pure delight. The stories taught her children to listen carefully and to remember. Her stories showed that kindness, gentleness, and a generous spirit bring rewards. Greed does not. Traditional tales of this type were called "Grandfather Tales" by folklorist Richard Chase, but Orville knows many of these stories as his mother's tales, passed along to her by his grandfather.

Familiar themes appear in some of these mountain stories. "The Bear, The Boy, and the Baking Soda" hints of the well-known tale "The Three Billy Goats Gruff." "Catskin" is a Cinderella story. While the Cinderella theme appears in stories from around the world, the setting and the voice in "Catskin" are Appalachian. Stories from far away found new voices in the mountain hollows.

Orville draws from his mountain childhood as he tells these tales in his own lively style. He has made long walks to the store at Matney, and he has taken shortcuts through the woods where he crossed mountain streams. He has eaten biscuits baked in a wood stove and milked the family cow. While he spins his yarns, listeners hear the authenticity in his voice and see his familiarity with the mountain settings for his tales. As he speaks, his own irrepressible laughter reveals his love of the long-told tales.

SOAP, SOAP, SOAP

*S*ee, back in the old days, people washed their clothes,
and they didn't have no washing machine like your mama has today
to throw clothes in and turn a button.
Back then, they had to wash them down at the river.
        And this woman went down to the river one day to wash her clothes.
Took an o-o-old big washtub and a washboard.
Got down to the river and looked
and didn't have no soap to wash her clothes in.
        She told her little boy standing there, she said,
"You go to the store,
and get me a cake of soap, and don't forget it, or I'll give you a whipping."
        Well, that little boy knowed what a whipping his mama could give him,
so he headed down the road to the store, going, "Soap, soap, soap.
Soap, soap, soap."
        And he come up on a mud hole.
Yeah, like most little mountain boys,
he stopped and got to playing in the mud hole.
Well, he played in the mud hole for about ten or fifteen minutes
and started on down the road to the store.
He got down the road a little piece, and do you know what?
Yeah, he forgot what his mama sent him to get.

Little boy said, "If I go back to the mud hole, maybe I can remember it."

Little boy, he run back to the mud hole.

He looked down in the mud hole, and he said,

"Right here I had it, and right here I lost it.

Oh, right here I had it, and right here I lost it."

Well, an old man was walking down the road, going to the store,

and he heard the little boy talking out there.

He went out to the mud hole, and he said,

"Son, you had it right here and you lost it right here."

He said, "What was it?

I'll help you find it."

Little boy said, "Right here I had it, and right here I lost it."

The old man said, "That little boy is crazy. I'm a-going on."

Old man starts down the road and he falls in the mud hole.

He jumped up and said, "Oo-ooh, this old mud is about slick as soap."

That little boy standing there said, "Yeah.

Soap, soap, soap."

The old man thought the little boy was making fun of him.

He jumped up out of the mud,

grabbed the little boy by the ear and shaked him real hard.

He said, "Say you're sorry you done it.

You just won't do it again."

The little boy said, "Well, I'm sorry I done it. I just won't do it again."

Down the road the little boy went, going to the store, saying,

"I'm sorry I done it. I just won't do it again.

Well, I'm sorry I done it. I just won't do it again."

Down the road a little piece, this woman was walking back from the store.

She had a big poke of groceries on her back.

And she fell off the bank—

fell in the ditch and the mud—

and them eggs and milk busted,

running all over her face, and that mud.

Here come that little boy down the road.

He walked up to her and said,

"Well, I'm sorry I done it. I just won't do it again."

The woman thought the little boy was making fun of her.

She jumped up out of the ditch,

grabbed the little boy by the ear, and threw him in the ditch.

She said, "Now I'm out and you're in. Ha, ha."

Little boy gets up out of the ditch,

goes on down the road, going to the store, saying,

"I'm out and you're in. Ha, ha.

Well, I'm out and you're in. Ha, ha."

Well, about a mile down the road, he come up on this farmer.

This farmer was coming back from town with a big wagonload of apples.

One of the wagon wheels had slid off the road,

and the farmer was in the mud, stuck.

He was trying to get out.

The little boy walked up to him and said, "I'm out and you're in. Ha, ha."

Well, the farmer thought the little boy was making fun of him.

He picked him up and give him a whipping.

He set him back down and said, "Son,

least you could say is, 'One's out. Get the other one out.'"

Well, the little boy went on down the road going to the store, saying,

"One's out. Get the other one out.

One's out. Get the other one out."

Well, down the road a little piece,

that little boy come up on a one-eyed man.

Little boy stopped and looked up and said,

"One's out. Get the other one out."

Boy, that one-eyed man got mad

and picked that little boy up. Smoked his britches good.

Set him back down and said,

"Son, the least you could say is, 'One's in. Put the other one in.'"

Little boy went on down the road, going to the store, saying,

"One's in. Put the other one in.

One's in. Put the other one in."

He come by the river.

This young woman was washing her clothes,

and she had two little babies playing on the bank.

One of the babies kicked the other one, and it fell in the river.

The little boy said, "One's in. Put the other one in."

And that woman looked around and seen her little baby in the river,

and she got it out right quick.

She turned around and she was mad.

She was going to give that little boy a whipping.

But she looked down at him and seen how dirty he was

and how muddy he was.

And she said, "Son, best thing you can do is go back home
and tell your mama she'd better give you a bath and use plenty of soap."

Little boy said, "Yeah.
Soap, soap, soap."

He went on down to the store and got his mama a big old cake of soap—
about that big.
Come back home.

His mama seen how dirty he was.
She put him in that tub and give him a good old sousing
up one side and down the other.
Then she took him out and pinned him up by his ears on the clothesline
to dry out while she finished her washing.

*Mama'd tell us that little tale and send us to the store,
and I never did forget what I went after.*

The Bear, the Boy, and the Baking Soda

 *N*ow wa-a-ay back up in the mountains
    in a log cabin

lived an old man, an old woman,

a little old boy, and a little old girl.

They had a pet squirrel—about that big.

    Well, that woman got up one day.

She was gonna bake a bi-i-ig pan of biscuits for breakfast.

And back then,

people didn't have biscuits you could throw in the oven, you know,

and just bake them.

Back then, you had to have baking soda to go in the flour and stuff

to make the biscuits rise.

    So this old woman got to looking;

she didn't have no baking soda.

She told her little boy, she said, "You run down to the store,

and get me a box of baking soda.

Be quick about it—

we're all getting hungry—

and I'll bake them biscuits.

    That little boy went down to the store,

and went in there and got him a box of baking soda.

He got the baking soda, and he started back home.

He went up the road there a little piece.

And he got up the road there, and he come to the edge of the woods.

That little boy said, "I believe I'll take a shortcut and go through the woods—
get home quicker."

Well, the little boy, he goes through the woods.

He come to the bridge—

walking through the woods.

He didn't know that under that bridge

laid a mean old hungry bear waking up from its winter nap.

That little boy started across the bridge real loud, a-walking.

Clomp, clomp, clomp, clomp.

That bear jumped up and said,

"Well, who dare go across my bridge?"

"It's I," said the little boy. "Me and my box of baking soda.

I'm headed home."

That bear said, "I'm hungry."

Jumped up on the bridge. Swallowed that little boy—just swallowed him whole.

Well, back at home,

the old man, the old woman, the little girl, and the little squirrel

waited and waited,

and the little boy didn't come home.

Finally, the old woman told the little girl, she said,

"You go to the store, and you tell your brother to get home.

We're getting hungry."

The little girl goes down to the store,

walks in there and says,

"Mr. Store Man, have you seen my little brother?"

"Well, yeah, he's been here and got a box of baking soda—headed home.

You'll probably find him playing beside the road somewhere."

Little girl starts home.

She goes up the road a-running,

come to the edge of the woods, and says,

"Uh-huh. I think I'll take a shortcut and beat my little brother home."

Little girl runs out through the woods till she comes to the bridge.

She starts across the bridge.

Clomp, clomp, clomp, clomp.

That bear jumped up and said,

"Well, who dare go across my bridge now?"

"It's I," said the little girl. "I'm headed home."

The bear said, "I done ate up a little boy and a box of baking soda.

I'm gonna eat you up."

Jumped up on the bridge. Swallowed the little girl—just swallowed her whole.

Well, back at home,

the old man, the old woman, and the little old squirrel waited and waited.

Finally, the old woman told her old man, she said,

"You go to the store and get them young'uns.

Tell them to get home. We're getting hungry."

Well, the old man walks down to the store and walks in there

and says, "Mr. Store Man, have you seen my little boy and little girl?"

"Yeah, they both been here, and they're headed home.

You'll probably find them playing beside the road there somewhere."

Well, the old man goes up the road,

and he walks and walks. He comes to the edge of the woods there, and he says,

"Well, I just believe I'll take a shortcut and beat my little boy and girl home."

He goes out through the woods. He comes to the bridge.

Old man started across the bridge, a-walking.

Clomp, clomp, clomp, clomp.

The old bear jumps up and says,

"Well, who dare go across my bridge now?"

"It's I," said the old man. "I'm headed home."

That bear says, "I done ate up a little boy and a box of baking soda.

Ate up a little girl.

I'm gonna eat you up."

Jumps up on the bridge and swallows the old man—just swallowed him whole.

Well, back at home that old woman and that little old squirrel waited and waited and waited.

Finally, the old woman said,

"If you want something done, you just have to do it yourself."

She went down to the store and said,

"Mr. Store Man, have you seen my family?"

"Well, yeah, old woman.

Your old man's been here and your little boy and little girl—headed home.

You'll probably find them playing beside the road somewhere."

She said, "I better not find my old man playing beside the road.

I'll be mad."

Well, she goes up the road.

She walked and walked till she come to the edge of the woods.

She said, "I believe I'll just take a shortcut and go through the woods.

I'll just beat everybody home."

The old woman taken out in the woods till she come to the bridge.

She walked across the bridge real loud.

Clomp, clomp, clomp, clomp.

The bear jumped up and said,

"Who dare go across my bridge now?"

"It's I," said the old woman. "I'm going home."

That bear said, "I done ate up a little old boy and a box of baking soda.

Ate up a little old girl.

Ate up an old man.

I'm gonna eat you up."

Jumped on the bridge, swallowed the old woman—just swallowed her whole.

Well, back at home,

that poor little old squirrel got hungrier and hungrier and hungrier.

That little squirrel said, "I'm going down to the store

and see what happened to my family.

I'm getting hungry."

Little squirrel hops down the road, goes in the store,

and hops up on that counter and says,

"Hey, Mr. Store Man, have you seen my family?"

"Well, yeah, little squirrel. They all been here and headed home."
He said, "They'll probably be home time you get back there."

That squirrel said, "I hope so. I'm getting hungry."
The little squirrel goes up the road.
Gets up the road a little piece and he come to the edge of the woods.
And that little squirrel said,
"I just believe I'll take a shortcut and go through the woods
and beat everybody home."
Little squirrel run through the woods till it come to the bridge.
He starts across the bridge going real fast.

Trip, trip, trip, trip.

And that bear jumped up and said,

"Who dare go across my bridge now?"

"It's I," said the little squirrel. "I'm headed home."

The bear said, "I done ate up a little old boy.
Ate up a little girl.
Ate up an old man.
Ate up an old woman.
I'm gonna eat you up."

That little squirrel said, "Ha, ha, Mr. Bear.
I just don't think you can catch me."
That little squirrel jumped plumb across the bridge in one jump
into a tree.
He looked back and started laughing and chattering at that bear.

And that bear said, "Huh!
A lazy little fellow like you can jump that far, I can too."
That old big bear give a big jump—
jumps about halfway across the bridge up in the air
and he falls.
And he hit the bridge so hard his belly busted open.

Out came a little boy and a box of baking soda.
Out came a little girl.
Out came an old man.
Out came an old woman.
Boy, they was so tickled to get out of there and see each other.
They got that little squirrel and went home.
    And that woman took that box of baking soda
and put it in the flour
and made a big old pan of biscuits.
They said that little old squirrel was so hungry,
it ate twelve biscuits by itself for breakfast.

When the acorns and hickory nuts start falling off the tree early, its gonna be a long winter.

If you see squirrels gathering nuts early, it's gonna be a hard winter.

If you see bees building their nest under the ground or close to the ground, it's gonna be a long, hard winter.

THE MAN ON THE MOON

*T*wo neighbors lived close together.

One of the mans, he was real nice and kind—
good old fellow. He'd give you the shirt off'n his back.

But his neighbor was mean, stingy and greedy
and didn't care for nothing or nobody.

One day,
this nice old man and this mean old man went to take a walk together.

They was walking down through the woods.

They came to a little old bird laying on the ground.

It'd fell out of a tree and broke its wing.

That nice old man reached down and picked that bird up.

"Poor little bird," he said. "You're hurt.

I'm going to take you home and take care of you."

That mean old man said, "Throw that bird down, and let's go on."

That nice man said, "No, I ain't mean and stingy and greedy like you are."

He said, "I'm gonna take that little bird home and take care of it."

Sure enough,
that nice old man took the little bird home.

He mended its wing.

He fed it, and he watered it,
and he took real good care of it.

Little bird got weller enough to fly away.

That man turned it loose, and it flew out the window.

In a few minutes, it come back, and it had a seed in its mouth.

It told that nice old man, it said,

"You take this seed and plant it out in your garden,

and that's where your fortune's gonna be."

Well, that nice old man took the seed out and planted it in his garden.

He watered the seed and hoed it and took good care of it.

One day, that old man went out in his garden and looked.

That seed had growed into a cucumber vine.

But it'd growed all through the field.

And one evening he looked out,

and them cucumber vines had cucumbers on 'em—about that long.

And that nice old man said, "I'm gonna try one of 'em for supper."

He went out and got one of them cucumbers—carried it in the house.

He cut it open with his knife, and it was full of gold.

Gosh, he run out and grabbed another one and brought it in the house.

Cut it open, and it was full of silver.

Every one of 'em was full of gold and silver.

He said, "I'm rich, I'm rich." Jumped up and down and hollered.

He said, "I've got to share the news with somebody."

He was tickled to death.

He went down and told that old mean man about it.

That old mean man jumped up and down and said,

"Why does everything happen to everybody but me?"

He said, "I'm gonna find me a little bird, and I'm gonna get rich like my neighbor."

Well, that old mean man went down the road the next day

looking for a bird,

and he didn't find one.

The next day he went down the road a-looking and didn't find no bird.

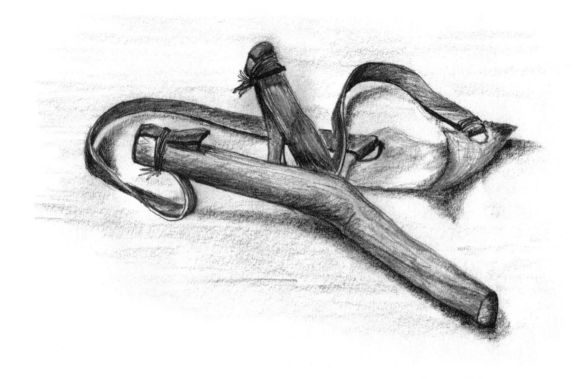

And the third day,
that mean old man made him a slingshot
and got him a big old rock and put it in the slingshot.
He was walking down the road,
and he seen a little bird sitting on the limb.
He pulled the slingshot back
and shot the little bird in the wing.
Little bird fell on the ground, its wing broke.

    That old mean man picked it up and said,
"Poor little bird." He said, "You're hurt."

    He said, "I'm gonna take you home and take care of you."
He carried that little bird home.
He mended its wing. He was good to it.
He watered it and fed it.

Little bird got weller enough to fly away,
and it flew out the window.
In a few minutes, it come back with a seed in its mouth.
It told that old mean man, "You take this and plant it in your garden.
That's where your fortune is gonna be."
That old mean man jumped up and down and hollered,
"Yeah, I'm gonna be rich like my neighbor!"
Tickled to death.
He runned out in the garden and planted that seed.
Well, he watered the seed and hoed it, took good care of it.
He looked out the window one day,
and that seed had growed into a cucumber vine,
but instead of growing through the field,
it growed straight up—plumb onto the moon.
That man looked, and it didn't have no cucumbers on it.
And he looked up and he said,
"That's where my fortune's gonna be—is on the moon."
That old mean man, he cloomed and he cloomed and he cloomed up that vine
till he got to the top of it.
When he got to the top, he stepped off the vine
and stepped onto the moon.
When he did, that vine, it withered and died and fell to the ground.
And that old mean man's up on the moon now,
jumping up and down, wanting off.
Ain't no way to get him off.
You go out there tonight and look up on the moon, and you'll see him.
And that's how that rascal got there.

I seen something last night
I'll never get over.

...The moon

GALLYMANDER

*T*his old woman lived wa-a-ay back
over in the mountains there.

She never got married, and she lived by herself.
She was kinda getting old.

She said, "I'm gonna go to town tomorrow,
see if I can hire me a girl to come back and work for me, help me out some."
She said, "I'm getting a little too old to do this all by myself."
The old woman went into town the next morning,
and she hired this girl.

Now this girl she hired,
she wasn't too smart. She was kinda lazy,
but she done enough work to get by.
The old woman'd tell her to sweep the floor;
she'd sweep the dust under the bed
instead of getting it up.
Tell her to make up the bed; she'd make up about half of the bed
and wash half of the dishes.
But she done enough she'd get by.

Well, that old woman kept her there about two or three months.
And the old woman had to go into town one morning for something.
And she told that girl, she said, "You clean the house up while I'm gone."

She said, "Whatever you do,
do-o-on't you look up the chimney while I'm gone."
Well, that old woman left and went into town.

Well, that girl there, she swept about half of the floor
and swept the dirt under the bed,
made up one bed and washed a few dishes.
And she got to thinking—said,
"What's up in that chimney that old woman didn't want me to see?
I wonder what it could be."

Well, that girl went to the chimney and looked up in the chimney.
Wa-a-ay up there in the crack was this big old leather bag.
And that girl got the fire hook out
and got to punching that leather bag, and it fell out.
That girl picked it up and looked in it.
And it was full of money—gold, silver.

"Gosh," that girl said, "I'm rich!"
And she grabbed that leather bag
and took down the road with it.
She run hard as she could run.
Got down the road a little piece,
and she come to this old cow.

This old cow said,
"Good girl, good girl, have you got time to stop and milk me?
Nobody ain't milked me in about a week.
I'll give you some milk to drink."

"No, old cow, I ain't got time to stop and mess with you."
She said, "Get somebody else to do it."
And so that girl kept on a-running
across another big field.
Come to an old barn and out there stood an old horse.

That old horse said, "Good girl, good girl,
have you got time to stop and rub my sore back?
I worked hard today.
Nobody ain't rubbed my back yet."

"No, no, no, I ain't got time to rub your old back.
Get somebody else to do it."
And that girl kept on a-running—
run through that field. She come to a peach tree.

That peach tree said,
"Good girl, good girl,
have you got time to stop
and break the dead limbs off of me?
They're hanging down, hurting me something awful."
It said, "I'll give you some peaches to eat."

That girl said, "I ain't got time to mess with you
and break no limbs off of you,
and if I want any peaches, I'll eat 'em anyway."
She cloom up in the tree and started eating the peaches.

Well, it wasn't long till that old woman come home.
She hollered and hollered for that girl.
And she got worried and went and looked up in the chimney
and seen her leather moneybag gone.
Boy, that old woman took down the road running and hollering,

*"Gallymander, gallymander, all my gold and silver's gone,
my grea-a-at long leather moneybag."*

And she run and run till she came to that cow.
She said, "Good cow,
have you seen a girl go by here with a jig and a jag and a long leather bag
with all my gold and silver in it?"

"Yeah, I seen that mean old thing. She went that way."
The cow said, "Ask the horse over yonder."

That woman went running through the field hollering,

"Gallymander, gallymander, all my gold and silver's gone,
my grea-a-at long leather moneybag."

She run till she come to the horse.
"Old horse," she said,
"Have you seen a girl go by here with a jig and a jag and a long leather bag
with all my gold and silver in it?"

"Yeah, I seen the mean old thing."
The horse said, "She went up that way.
Go ask the peach tree. She might have seen her."

That woman kept a-running and hollering,

"Gallymander, gallymander,
all my gold and silver's gone.
Gallymander, gallymander."

Run till she come to the peach tree.
She said, "Peach tree, have you seen a girl go by here
with a jig and a jag and a long leather bag with all my gold and silver in it?"

"Yeah, I've seen her." The peach tree said, "She's up here eating peaches.
Do you want the mean old thing?"

That woman said, "I sure do."

That peach tree shook and shook.
Shook the girl on the ground.
The leather moneybag come out,
and that woman broke a limb off the peach tree and give that girl a whipping.
Told her to get gone.
And that woman got her leather moneybag and went back home.

Well, she put the moneybag back up in the chimney.

And I guess another month or two went by, and that old woman said, "Well,

every girl can't be like her."

She said, "I'm going to go back to town and hire another one."

She went back to town and hired this other girl,

and brought her home.

Sure enough, this girl was smart.

Man, she'd wash all the dishes, sweep the floor, make up the bed.

They said she'd work and was a good person.

This old woman was tickled to death with her.

Well, a couple of months went by,

and that old woman had to run into town to get something.

And she told that girl, she said,

"You clean the house while I'm gone and do everything,

but whatever you do,

do-o-on't look up the chimney while I'm gone."

That woman left and went into town.

Well, this good girl,

she made up all the beds, swept the floor real good, and washed all the dishes.

Didn't have nothing left to do.

She got to thinking, why didn't that woman want me to look up the chimney?

And sure enough, this girl went to the chimney and looked up it.

Wa-a-ay up there in the crack was that long leather moneybag.

She got the fire hook,

a-hitting that moneybag and hitting it,

and it fell down.

And she opened it, and it was full of gold and silver.

That girl got scared and said,

"Oh, no. That old woman'll know I've been looking up that chimney."

She tried to put the leather moneybag back in the chimney,
but it fell back down and she couldn't get it back up there,
and it scared her.
And she took off a-running and left the bag laying there in the ashes.
And that good girl run down the road, running hard as she could run.

      She come to that cow, and that cow said,
"Good girl, good girl, have you got time to stop and milk me?"
The cow said, "Nobody ain't milked me in a week.
I'll give you a glass of milk to drink."

      That girl said, "Yeah, I got time."
She milked that old cow,
and that cow give her a grea-a-at big old glass of milk to drink.
And that girl took off. Run across the field and come to the horse.

      That old horse said, "Good girl, good girl.
"Have you got time to stop and rub my poor back?
I worked hard all day today, and my back's sore."

That good girl said, "Yea, I got time to rub your back."
And she rubbed that old horse's back.

She got done and the horse said,
"Now, you get on my back and I'll give you a ride."
Rode that girl across into the next field.

And that girl run through that field and she come to the peach tree.
That old peach tree said, "Good girl, good girl,
have you got time
to stop and break these dead limbs off of me, hanging down here,
hurting me awful?"
It said, "I'll give you some peaches to eat."

That good girl said, "Yea, I've got time to do that."
She walked around that peach tree,
and broke all the dead limbs off of it.

The peach tree said, "Now get up here and eat some peaches."
And the girl cloom up in the peach tree and started eating the peaches.

Well, about that time, the old woman come home.
She hollered and hollered and hollered for that girl.
Couldn't find her.
And she run to the chimney and looked up in the chimney,
and her leather moneybag was gone.
She didn't see it laying in the ashes.
And she took off a-running.

"Gallymander, gallymander, all my gold and silver's gone,
my grea-a-at long leather moneybag."

She run till she come to the cow.
She said, "Good cow,
have you seen a girl go by here with a jig and a jag and long leather bag,
got all my gold and silver in it?"

That cow said, "No, I ain't seen nobody today.
Not nobody."

That old woman kept on running through the field, hollering,

*"Gallymander, gallymander, all my gold and silver's gone,
my grea-a-at long leather moneybag."*

She run till she came to the horse.
She said, "Old horse, have you seen a girl go by here
with a jig and a jag and long leather bag,
all my gold and silver in it?"

"No, no, I ain't seen nobody at-all today.
Not nobody."

That woman went on a-running, hollering,

"Gallymander, gallymander, all my gold and silver's gone."

She run till she come to the peach tree.
She said, "Peach tree,
have you seen a little girl come by here with a jig and a jag
and long leather bag, all my gold and silver in it?"

That peach tree said, "No, I ain't seen nobody today,"
and the girl was in the peach tree eating peaches.

That woman took off a-hollering,

*"Gallymander, gallymander, all my gold and silver's gone,
my grea-a-at long leather moneybag."*

And she kept on a-running and a-hollering "Gallymander"
till she fell plumb over.

This old man come by in a wagon—
coming home from town—seen her laying there.
He put her in the wagon and took her back home.

You know,
nobody never told me if she ever found that leather moneybag or not.
But they say that to this day
that woman never did hire another girl to come help her work.

This was one of Mama's favorite tales.
I remember her telling it many a time.
She probably thought it suited the boys and the girls both.
We'd sit there and listen to that tale—
bunching that galax.
Mama'd say, "Gallymander, gallymander,"
and our eyes would get about that big sometimes.

Twelve pears a-hanging high
as twelve men go riding by.
Each took a pear
and left eleven hanging there.

How could this happen?
       (The man's name was Each.)

CATSKIN

*A*wa-a-ay back out in the woods
      lived this old man and this old woman.
But they had this girl that worked for them.
She was bound out to that old man and woman.
     They was real poor, and this girl didn't have but one dress.
And every time a hole come in her dress,
they'd sew a cat's tail to her dress.
It wasn't long till that girl with that dress on with the cat tails hanging out
looked like a cat running around.
They started calling her Catskin.
     Well, one day,
this old woman died—that Catskin worked for.
Catskin had to stay there and work for the man.
     One time, the man was out in the field a-working,
and Catskin got in the house, got in the old dresser drawer.
Found that woman's wedding dress,
and she put it on.
     Catskin come to the door.
And the old man was working in the field and seen her.
Gah, she was so pretty, he fell in love with her.
And so he runned up there and said, "Catskin, will you marry me?"

She said, "Well, I might marry you
if you go out and have me a dress made
that's the color of a-a-all the fishes that swim in the sea."

That man went out and had a dress made.
It was the color of a-a-all the fishes that swum in the sea.
He brought it back and said, "That is a beautiful dress."
He said, "Now, Catskin, will you marry me?"

She said, "I might if you go out and have me a dress made
that's the color of a-a-all the birds that fly in the air."

He runned out and had her a dress made
that was the color of a-a-all the birds that flew in the air.
They said it was a lot more prettier than the other one. It was beautiful.

"Now," he said, "Catskin, will you marry me?"

She said, "I might
if you'll go out and have a dress made
that's the color of a-a-all the flowers that grow in the world."

He went out and had a dress made
that was the color of a-a-all the flowers that growed in the world.
They said it was a beautiful dress.

"Now, Catskin, will you marry me?"

Catskin said, "I might if you'd give me your flying box."

That old man had a flying box there he flew around in once in a while,
through the air and stuff.
He didn't want to give it up, but he wanted to marry Catskin. He said, "Okay."
He give Catskin that flying box.

Well, Catskin grabbed all three of her pretty dresses
and jumped in that flying box and said, "Fly, box, fly."
And it took out of there, and she flew and left the man standing there.
And she was flying over mountains, over valleys and,
gosh, having a good time flying around in that flying box.

And she was flying one day
and looked down and seen a big old house out in the woods.
And she lit the flying box,
landed on the ground.
And she folded it up,
and they was a big rock there.
She got them three dresses that man made for her
and put 'em in that flying box
and hid the flying box under a rock.
And she had that dress on that had all the cat tails, you know, hanging on it.
     Went up to that big house and knocked on the door.
Old woman come to the door and said,
"Shoo, scat, you get away from here, you cat!"
     Catskin said, "I ain't a cat. I'm a young girl looking for a job."
     "You dirty old thing. You ain't gonna work here looking like that."
     That woman had a girl. She said, "Mama, don't be mean to her."
She said, "Give her a job."
     "Well, I'll give her a job washing dishes,
but she ain't working in the kitchen a-cooking looking like that."
She give Catskin a job.
     Well, Catskin worked there awhile.
And the king had a son,
and he was looking for a wife for his son.
And one day the king sent word all through the mountains,
every girl that was single
to come to a dance he was having at the king's house that night.
     Well, that woman said to her daughter,
"Me and you are going tonight to the king's dance.
Get on your pretty dress."
     Catskin said, "Can I go?"

That woman said, "No, you dirty thing.
You stay here and wash the dishes while I'm gone."
    While Catskin was washing the dishes,
that girl and her mama left.
They got out of sight.
Catskin run down there
and put that dress on that was the color of all the fishes that swim in the sea.
Got in her flying box and flew to the king's house.
    She walked right up there with that dress on.
Them boys' eyeballs popped out,
and the king's son, he seen her.
He grabbed her and started dancing with her.
They danced and danced nearly to midnight.
When they got close to the door,
Catskin jerked away from him and run out.
Got in her flying box,
flew back down there
and hid the pretty dress and the box
and put that old cat tail dress back on again.
    Well, time that girl and her mama got home,
Catskin was down there washing dishes.
    That girl said, "Catskin you ought to have been to the dance tonight."
She said, "There was the most prettiest girl come
that had on the prettiest dress you ever seen."
    Catskin said, "Well, I'd liked to went, but your mama wouldn't let me go."
    "Well, he's gonna have another one tomorrow night."
    That woman said, "That dirty old thing ain't going.
She'll stay here and mop the floors."
    Next night, that girl and her mama left.
They got out of sight, and Catskin run down

and put the dress on that was the color of a–a-all the birds that flew in the air.
Got in the flying box and flew to the king's house.
Gosh, them boys' eyes bugged out. She come in with that pretty dress on.
The king's son, he was falling in love with her.
He grabbed her and danced and danced with her.
Wouldn't let nobody else around her—
danced, danced nearly till midnight.
Got near the door
and Catskin jerked away from him,
running out the door.
Got in the flying box and flew back home.

Hid the flying box,
put the old dress back on again.

About that time, that woman and the girl got home.
Catskin was in there mopping the floor.

The girl said, "Catskin, you ought to been there tonight.
That girl come back, and she had the prettiest dress on.
I'd do anything to own a dress like that," she said.
"She was beautiful!"

Catskin said, "Well, I wanted to go,
but your mama wouldn't let me."

"Well, they're going to have one more dance."

That woman said, "That dirty old thing ain't going.
She's gonna stay here and clean out the fireplace.
That's what she's gonna do."

The next night, the girl and her mama left.
Catskin run down there
and put on that dress
that was the color of a-a-all the flowers that growed in the world.
Got in the flying box,
flew to the king's house.

With that dress on, she looked so pretty the king's son just about fell over.
He grabbed her and said,
"I've fallen in love with you.
You ain't getting away from me tonight."
He took a ring off his finger
and put it on her finger and said,
"You belong to me."

They danced and danced nearly till midnight.
She got close to the door.
She jerked away from him, run out, and got in her flying box.

144

Time everybody got outside, she was gone
back to the house.

      Well, that girl and her mama come home.
Catskin had that old dress on,
mopping, cleaning out the fireplace.

      That was the last dance they had.
But the king's son had done and fell in love with Catskin.
He got lovesick so bad,
the king sent mans all through the mountains looking for her.
They were looking everywhere—couldn't find her.
The king's son got so lovesick he got in bed.
Doctor said he was gonna die from love sickness
if they didn't find that girl.
The king was sending anybody—
anything that could help him.

      One day, Catskin said,
"Let me bake him a cake and send it to him."

      That woman said,
"You dirty old thing, you ain't baking no cake."

      The girl said, "Mama, let her bake him a cake."

      She said, "Okay, you bake him a cake,
but I'll take it to him."

      And Catskin baked him up a big old chocolate cake,
and she took that ring off that the king's son give her
and put it in the middle of that cake.

      Well, the old woman took it to the king's house.
She went in the bedroom.
There the king's son laid in bed, looking about dead.
She cut him a piece of that cake off,
and that ring fell out.

Gosh, he seen that ring, and his eyeballs fell out. He jumped up.
He said, "Where'd you get that cake at?"

    That woman said, "I baked it."

    He said, "No, you didn't bake it.
You go bring me the girl that baked that cake or I'll have your head."

    Gosh, it scared that woman. She went back and got Catskin,
and they come back to the king's house.
Catskin walked in there.

    He said, "There's the girl I'm a-looking for.
Where's your pretty dress at?"

    Catskin went out and put the dress on
that's the color of all the fish that swim in the sea
and come back in.

    "No, no, not that dress."

    She went back out and put the one on
that's the color of a-a-all the birds that flew in the air
and come back in.

    He said, "No, no, not that dress."

She went back outside and put the dress on
that's the color of all the flowers that growed in the world.
She come in there, and he said, "That's the dress!"

Him and Catskin got married.
They got in that flying box, and they flew out of there and never was seen again.
I reckon they lived happy every after.

I'd say it takes a special kind of mind
to tell stories like that.
Mama'd tell tales,
and Orville'd sit and look right at her.
                    —Willis Hicks, Orville's brother

A Folktale in the Making

Orville wrote the following story about of his cousin Ray Hicks, but Ray died before Orville had a chance to share the story with Ray. Neither has he told it publicly prior to this publication. The story reads like a Jack Tale—with a similar format, but not as complex.

The story draws from Ray's experience as a boy. His father died when Ray was young, so Ray, the oldest child, provided for his mother, brothers, and sisters. Ray recalled a time when his father had given away a bushel of potatoes to someone in need. This incident appears in the story but with a twist that lets Ray receive the generosity. Throughout his life, Ray raised potatoes and other vegetables in the large garden below his house. The produce nurtured not only his mother, brothers, and sisters but also his wife and children.

While many stories have begun orally, this one began on paper as Orville wrote his story idea. But Orville is a storyteller. To tell the story, he would put the paper aside and tell the tale as he recalls it.

If Orville told this story a number of times, it would become deeper and richer with the telling—and if someone else heard it and told it, the story would change a little here and there. Before long, it could be like another Jack Tale, but with Ray as the main character.

①

The Little Boy of Blue Ridge Mt.

Now. Ray Lived way up in the Blue
Ridge Mt. with his mama and his
Little Brothers and sisters. Now Rays
Daddy had Died. So that Left Ray
There with his mama And his Brother
and Sisters. Now o pete was on The
Table They had nothing Left To eat
Rays mama Turn To Ray with Tears in
her eyes. She Said Ray Daddys gone
you are The olDest. So you will have To
go out and Find us sumep To eat
Dont we all are going To starve To
Death. well Ray headed Down The
Road Bare FooteD Barley olD enough To
Take care of him self shoeLess
Ray walk over The Mt Though Bike
Thickets and Them BIars sticking his
Foot But Ray wasen't thinking of
him self. He was a Thinkig of his
mama at home with all of them
food am them a starving So

THE LITTLE BOY OF THE BLUE RIDGE MOUNTAINS

 ow, Ray lived way up in the Blue Ridge Mountains with his mama and his little brothers and sisters. Ray's daddy had died, so that left Ray there with his mama and his brothers and sisters.

Now, old Pete was on the table; they had nothing left to eat. Ray's mama turned to Ray with tears in her eyes. She said, "Ray, Daddy's gone, and you are the oldest, so you will have to go out and find us something to eat. [If you] don't, we all are going to starve to death."

Well, Ray headed down the road, barefooted, barely old enough to take care of himself. Ray walked over the mountain through blar [briar] thickets, and them blars [briars] sticking his foot. But Ray wasn't thinking of himself. He was a-thinking of his poor mama at home with all of them kids to feed and them a-starving so.

Ray walked till he come to a house. The man inside met him at the door, and he said, "I'm sorry, son, but I barely got enough food to feed my family. You will have to go somewhere else."

So Ray went on down the road. He walked nearly 20 miles. Poor old Ray was give plumb out, his feet a-bleeding, but Ray didn't give up.

It wasn't long till he came to another house. He knocked on the door, and an old man came to the door. He had a long beard, gray hair, and smiling eyes. He looked at Ray with a big smile and said, "Can I help you, son?"

Ray said, "Yeah. I need some work. Mama and my brothers and sisters are about to starve to death."

The old man said, "Ray, I am going to give you a bushel of 'taters to take home for your family, but you will have to come back and work a week for me to pay for them."

Ray thanked the old man and promised him he'd be back to work for him. Ray picked up that 60-pound bushel of 'taters, put them on his back, and he walked that 20 miles back home. His mama, brothers and sisters were tickled to death to have something to eat.

Ray told his mama, "I'm going to give you half of the 'taters to eat, and I am going to plant the other half out in my little garden so we will have something to eat this winter."

Well, Ray cut them 'taters up, then planted them in the garden. Then Ray left and walked the 20 miles back across the mountain to help the old man that gave him the 'taters.

The old man said, "Well, Ray, I can see that you are an honest man. You kept your word about coming to work."

Well, Ray stayed and helped the old man for a week. The old man worked Ray 10 hours a day—grubbing new ground and planting 'taters, setting cabbage for his winter food. Well, finally, the week went by. Ray's work was done.

The old man looked at Ray with a twinkle in his eye. He said, "Ray, you worked so hard, I am going to give you another bushel of 'taters to take home and some cabbage plants to plant and some carrot seeds I've got left. Then he reached in his pocket and gave Ray a five-dollar bill. He said, "Here, son. You have earned every penny of it."

Ray went on back home. He give his mama the bushel of 'taters. Then he give her the five-dollar bill to buy some sugar and stuff for winter. Then Ray went out and planted the cabbage plants and carrot seeds in the garden. Then Ray went in to cutting wood for the winter. He drug it down the mountain. Then he cut it and stacked it on the porch. When Ray got all the wood cut for winter, it was time to dig the 'taters that Ray had planted. He dug nearly 20 bushels of 'taters. He put the 'taters in the cellar for winter. Then he cut the cabbage heads and dug two bushels of carrots and put them in the cellar.

Well, they had God and Ray to thank that winter, for they neither went cold or hungry that winter.

This old world needs a lot more
[people like] Ray Hicks in it.
Then it would be a better place to live.

Author's Note:
Stories Behind
Orville's Stories

I did not know what path my life was about to take when I first looked up Orville's telephone number and called him. I was interested in his herb-gathering experience. My curiosity about herbs opened conversation about how his mother told stories to the children. He caught my attention.

For five years, I have worked with Orville to hear and record his personal story and to transcribe some of his tales. I have heard him tell his tales many times and in many settings. Wherever Orville is, he offers each story as a gift to those who listen. He is true to his roots and steady, yet full of surprises that spring from his love of his mountain heritage, his playful manner, and his generous spirit. These surprises often have given me valuable glimpses of his heritage and of the tradition of folklore.

After taping and transcribing over 20 tales, I visited Orville to review the transcribed stories. While I was there, Orville told me the story of "Jack and the King's Mountain." Orville told this tale as a somewhat shorter yarn than most other Jack Tales. Yet in this story, the clever Jack shows his typical wit as he answers the king's riddle about how many baskets would be needed to move a mountain. I had come to visit Orville without my tape recorder, so I listened and made a few notes. I could not write fast enough to capture all of his words.

Later, I decided I should add this story to the book. I called Orville to tell him my plan. He told the story again over the phone as I wrote fragments of Jack's adventure. When I let Orville know how sketchy my notes were, he gladly told the story again. While the plot remained the same, the word choices varied a little. I was left to decipher my notes from three accounts, not just one.

A week later, I called back with questions about the gaps in my story notes. Again, Orville told the story over the phone. Again, word arrangements changed. I had tried unsuccessfully to record over the phone, so I opted to take my tape recorder and visit Orville. On that visit, Orville repeated his story with additional rich detail.

Orville acknowledged that he had heard the tale only once—about 20 years earlier at Beech Mountain. He had since told it to friends and family occasionally but had not told it publicly. As Orville relayed this story multiple times, I watched the development of a folktale in the hands of this storyteller. If other people told the same story, they would add their own twists, as I had heard Orville do.

Phone conversations with Orville have been interesting, to say the least. One day he called to tell me that he had run across the story that he had written for Ray Hicks. He read it to me over the phone. In the story, I could hear several common elements of Jack Tales, but the character was young Ray, faced with the Jack-like task of feeding his family after his own father's death.

While Orville's story was fiction, it began with a seed of truth. Young Ray, the oldest child, actually had faced the challenge of providing for his mother, brothers, and sisters after his father died. In the story, a kind man offers potatoes to Ray in return for work. The incident reflects a time when Ray's father gave a bushel of potatoes to someone in need. In the tale, Ray fed his family with the potatoes but saved some to plant for a new crop. Ray, in fact, kept a fine garden with a generous potato crop that fed his family every year.

While the story was, until that time, an untold tale, I realized that it represented the way in which folktales began: with bits of truth and pieces of the familiar, woven with imagination into a patchwork of story. I wondered what would happen if Orville told this story again and again. As with the retelling of "Jack and the King's Mountain," the details would surely become richer. Then, I wondered, what would happen if someone else told the story. Would the story remain Ray's? Would other tales of Ray be told? Or would that rascal Jack somehow step into this tale as he has stepped into other stories?

Such thought about Orville's stories leaves me wondering where Jack Tales began. What seed of truth is woven into "Jack and the Varmints" or "Big Jack and Little Jack"? As with Orville's story of Ray, there must have been some incident or circumstance that led to a story about Jack—and then changed little by little with the voices of countless storytellers—and then criss-crossed with other tales—and so on.

Again, Orville called. "I wrote a story for that grandson of yours," he said. "If you've got time, I'll read it to you?"

"Sure," I said. Only two days earlier, I had told him that my awaited grandchild would be a boy.

This freshly written story, "Orville and the Little People," was purely a gift, another gem, beginning on paper, reflecting the experience of a master storyteller, woven into a patchwork of truth and imagination.

*O*rville Hicks wrote this first draft of "Orville and the Little People" on March 21, 2008. As a storyteller, he focuses on the story line, imagined as if told in his own voice. The flow of the story reveals his skill in crafting the oral tale, rich with images and details of his mountain heritage. Orville's story echoes the long-told tales, while his portrayal of young Orville reflects the gentle nature of the storyteller himself.

① Orville and The Little People

Way Back in The mountians Down in a Holor Lived orville. with His mama and Daddy. and his Brother and sisters. Now they were Real poor. Not in Food or Love They were poor in money. it was Fall oF The Year. The Big maple Tree in The yard Had turn To gold. The Big Hickory Tree on The mt. were Droping There Hickory Nuts. But orville and his Family needed some Money To pay There taxies. DiDn't get no money They were going To Lose there Farm orville was Born on The Farm He Didn't want to lose there home or land He Love The place. playing on the Hay Stacks getting water Froe The Spring For mama But orville Did'nt no what to Do.

One evening orville mama said
Orville go To uncle adie and Borrow
me some sugar. orville Loved To go
To uncle adie For adie would tell
him a tale also he would get to see
Bennie adie son, him and Bennie
always had a good Time Togeather
so orville walked across The mt. To
uncle adie. he stayed awhile played
and talk To Bennie. it was a getting
Late orville said I Better get home
orville Decided To go By The hickory
Tree, and check on his Rabbit Trap
and check one The Hickory nuts
orville got ABout Half way Down
The mt, He came To The Big olD
Hickory Tree. orville heard a
Racket. he peeped From Behind
The Hickory Tree, There at The
Rabbit Trap, was about Ten
Little men They were Trying
To get The Rabbit Box open

③

But no matter how hard They
Tried They goulD no yet The Lid
open it was To heavy For The
Little men They were not More
The 6 inche High. Orville Heard
a cry comming From The Box
Help Help please Help. Orville Came
out From Behind The Tree The
Little men Seen orville comming
it Scared Them neary To Death
They Took off a Running. Then
They come To a hole in The grouND
They all darted Down into the
Hole out of Sight. Orvile went
Over To The Box he openeD The
LiD of The Box. There was a
Little man Dgwn in The Box
he was Scared To Death. Orville
Said Please Dont Be afraid of
Me I want hurt you
But what were you a doing
In my Rabbit Box The Little men
said we are hugrany I was a
Trying The get That apple

161

The other Little people Stuck
There Head out OF The hole in
grounD. They seeD That orville
was not going To hurt There
Friend so They all came out
They came over and Set Down
orville Took his Knife and
peeled The apple Then he cut
it up into Little Bitty pieces
and DevideD it With The Little
people, They made good Friend
Orville and the Little people
Orville would go up There To
That hickory Tree. he would
Take The Little people Some
apples or cookies That his
Mama had made or some Fresh
Cow milk. For Them To Drink
Orville would Tell Them Jack
Tales They wood set and
Laugh at The Tales Then They
Wood Tell Orville Tales about
Little people

They all how made good Frends
one Day They ask orville weher
Do you Live at orville Said I
Live Down There in The hollor
In that Big ole House the one
with the Big porch around it
and all The pretty Flowers
But I want Be Living There
Long IF we Dont get The
Money To pay our Taxis. The
Little people Felt Sorry For
Orville They asked if They
Could Help, orville Said There
wasn't nothing The Could Do
To Help,
one evening orville mama
Said orville go up and get
us some Hickory nut. and I
will Bake us a cake

So orville got his homemade
Basket went up on The mt.
To the Hickory tree

163

⑥ 𝒶𝒶

He Started To Pick up The
Hickory nuts. The Little people
Ran out Frome The Hole in the
ground. They asked orville iF They
Could. Help. He Said why sure
you all can help. it Took 2or3 OF
The Little men To pick up one
Hickorynuts But it wasn't Long
Till They got The Baske Full
orville Thanked The Little
people. Them he went on home
his mama Said put The nuts
Behind The wood stove Theen
go Do yours choirs Them we
eat supper. and them we will
Tell some Tales and Break The
Hickorynuts up For a cake
well orville got his choirs Done
Then They all eat supper Them
They all got Behind The old wood
Stove They Started To Break up
the Hickorynuts. Mama hollerd,
Real Loud Daddy said what is it

Mama said These hickory nuts
are made OF pure gold.
Shore enough every Hickory nut
Thoses Little men had pick up
had Turned To pure gold.
they sold The gold Hickory nut
and paid There Taxis they
Did not Lose There house and
Land afterall Thanks To The
Little people orville went up
To the hickory Tree He Took
a hammer and Some wood he
Buit Thoese Little people
The prettis Little House you ever
Did see To Live in and he planted
The Some apple trees around
The house Because They Love
apples so good. You might
pass That Hickory Tree some
night if You Do. You Just
might here orville out There
Telling Those Little people
Jack Tales

Orville Hicks and *Jack Tales and Mountain Yarns:*
A Scholar's (and Friend's) Afterword
by Thomas McGowan

Orville Hicks is one of North Carolina's most skilled and entertaining traditional storytellers. He continues the traditions and prowess of what folklorist Carl Lindahl has called our "Nation's Most Celebrated Storytelling Family"—the Hicks-Harmon clan.[1] This collection, excellently organized and edited by Julia Ebel, presents an especially representative sample of the rich art of Orville's notable storytelling.

A central figure in Orville's early growing up was his mother, Sarah Ann Harmon Hicks. His romantic remembering of her provides a special frame for his own storytelling. This collection opens with his recalling her galax gathering and telling stories to keep the children entertained and busy with farm work. She sang old songs, challenged young Orville with riddles, and gave to him a special foundation in local tales and the Appalachian Jack Tale. Often at the start of a storytelling session, Orville evokes her special place.

Orville develops a set of memories of growing up in the pastoral simplicity of rural life in the mid-twentieth century Southern Mountains, but he also gives a sense of the special role of story and song traditions within his family. In his autobiographical account here, he moves from being "real small," unable to accompany Sarah Hicks on her gathering expeditions, waiting on the porch with his sister Mary and brother Jerry for the return of a hardworking mother. Despite being tuckered out, Sarah Hicks always brought home some small treats for the children. In helping her bunch galax leaves, Orville admits that at seven he probably "played more than [he] pulled" (8).

Sharing these memories connects people to a rich past, but also to Orville as a person. He establishes this close relationship in storytelling sessions and in this collection through his remembering growing up in the mountains. But once he establishes this relation and trust, he can play with truth and break into half-true stories. "Squirrel Hunting" and "Mule Eggs" illustrate the creative fun of his building on local activities with tall-tale flourishes of personal exaggeration and trickery.[2]

I have a special memory of Orville and the son of Mike Harman, the Ashe County-weaver who received the North Carolina Heritage Award with Orville in Raleigh in October 2007.[3] The program organizers provided a hospitality room in the hotel where award winners and their families could gather. Orville had plenty of folks to talk to, but he separated himself to tell stories to young Jake Harman. Afterwards, Jake asked me if Orville's "Mule Eggs" story were really true. Orville sometimes even fools my Appalachian State University students when he tells the story with its local details and placement among a set of nostalgic reminiscences.

Orville Hicks is the most talented contemporary teller continuing the traditional Appalachian stories of the boy-trickster Jack. Writing of activities along the eighteenth-century Appalachian frontier, the local historian Joseph Doddridge remarked on the popularity of these stories and their being "handed down from generation to generation from time immemorial."[4] In the 1920s, Isabel Gordon Carter collected a set of them from Jane Hicks Gentry, who had moved from Watauga County to Hot Springs, North Carolina, where she ran a well-known boarding house, now celebrated by a state historical marker. Carter's collection appeared in the *Journal of American Folklore* in

1925.[5] Richard Chase collected Jack Tales from "R.M. Ward and his kindred in the Beech Mountain section of Western North Carolina and other descendants of COUNCIL Harmon (1803-1896)," and popularized the tales widely in his much-published *The Jack Tales*.[6] Orville Hicks, a great-grandson of Counce Harmon, continues the family telling of these traditional stories in his own special way.

This book includes Orville's masterful telling of a set of what folklorists have labeled the Beech Mountain Jack Tale.[7] Orville heard versions at home from his mother and on his frequent visits to the home of Ray and Rosa Hicks, which became famous in storytelling circles and documentary films. Orville frequently drove Ray to the National Storytelling Festival in Jonesboro, Tennessee, and other engagements throughout the South.[8] In their local community and on the road, Orville served a loving apprenticeship with Ray in the telling of the Beech Mountain Jack Tale. At Ray's funeral, Orville sang his "Ballad of Ray Hicks," written to memorialize Ray's influence; the new compact disc of Orville's stories includes his singing this tribute to "big Ray." [9]

In this collection, Orville tells of his favorite adventures of "clever, witty, smart" Jack, who is his hero, "just a ordinary boy [who] had a lot of sense" (35). His development of these tales is tighter and more focused than Ray Hicks's digressive performances. Orville's valuing Jack's wittiness appears in his rendering of conversations between Jack and the King or giants. His creation of dialog is entertaining, but also shows Jack's special ability to react to challenges and to use talk to his advantage.

Another special aspect of this book is Orville's development of new stories resulting from the special rapport between him and Julia Ebel. Their friendship and her encouragement created occasions for original narratives including publishing a fictional tale to honor Ray Hicks and another story written as a gift to her grandson. Ebel provides an enlightening discussion of Orville as composer of new stories in action.

Besides Jack Tales, Sarah Harmon told other fictional children's stories to Orville and his brothers and sisters. Richard Chase lists her as a source for "Gallymanders" in the collection he entitled *The Grandfather Tales*.[10] Orville sometimes uses Chase's book title to refer to these stories, and this collection includes an interesting set of them. Like his Jack Tales, his telling of these incorporates his delightful development of dialog, expressive of Orville's own practice and interest in conversation as social action that establishes relationships. These speech exchanges make Orville's versions of the tales special opportunities for students to act out the tales in the classroom.

Two past publications of Jack Tales had notable illustrations. Berkeley Williams, Jr.'s sketches in Chase's *The Jack Tales* and Gail E. Haley's drawings in *Mountain Jack Tales* offer their own bright representation of Jack's Mountain persona.[11] Sherry Jensen has taken Orville Hicks's evocation of past times and portrayal of clever Jack to contribute a new set of visual interpretations here that imaginatively build on the stories.

The collaboration of Orville Hicks and writer Julia Ebel has produced a rich collection of his stories in this book.[12] Ebel has arranged them to represent effectively his oral style and repertory, and she has given readers and teachers special helps to understand and appreciate this special North Carolina storyteller and his art.

Orville Hicks continues important traditions of North Carolina narrative and brings to their performance a personal creativity and delightful spirit that enrich traditional forms and enliven their structure and use in present-day contexts. He practices his verbal art in a variety of formal contexts—festivals, schools and universities, family reunions, conventions—but he also brings storytelling and joke telling to his work and regular social contacts. His stories and his way of life embody important Mountain values and deepen our appreciation of the rich speech and folk culture of Appalachian North Carolina. He remembers old times with a strong affection for family and past ways. He recounts the adventures of the trickster hero Jack with a special delight. The best way to hear Orville is in person at a storytelling event, but this collection certainly provides an excellent second-best way to encounter his stories—and a special opportunity to hold onto them and enjoy them again and again, and to think about their artfulness and meanings.

NOTES

1. Lindahl uses this encomium as the title of chapter 1 in his *American Folktales from the Collections of the Library of Congress* (Armonk, NY: M.E. Sharpe, 2004), 1. This two-volume edition of American folktales includes a notable section on Ray Hicks and other Hicks-Harmon relatives, including Roby Monroe Hicks, Buna Hicks, Maud Gentry Long, and Samuel Harmon, transcribed from field recordings in the Library's Archive of Folk Culture.

2. I discuss the challenges and pleasures of Orville's bending of truth in "'Sort of like an *Appalachian Journal* Editor': Presenting and Playing with Identity in the Storytelling of Orville Hicks," *Appalachian Journal* 29.1-2: 164-79.

3. Orville's and Mike Harman's award citations with photographs are printed in *North Carolina Heritage Awards 2007* (Raleigh: N.C. Arts Council, 2007), 4-7.

4. Doddridge's "Notes," which include "A View of the State of Society and Manners of the First Settlers," are published in Samuel Kercheval, *A History of the Valley of Virginia* (Winchester, VA: Samuel H. Davis, 1833), 251-445. The comments on "narrations concerning Jack" occur on pp. 374-75 in the original edition and 278 in some later editions. The first connection of Doddridge's observations and the Jack Tales is made by Charles Perdue, Jr., "Old Jack and the New Deal: The Virginia Writer's Project and Jack Tale Collecting in Wise County, Virginia" *Appalachian Journal* 14.2: 108-52. Perdue has published a collection of Jack Tales collected in southwest Virginia: *Outwitting the Devil: Jack Tales from Wise County, Virginia* (Santa Fe, NM: Ancient City Press, 1987).

5. Isabel Gordon Carter, "Mountain White Folklore : Tales from the Southern Blue Ridge," *Journal of American Folklore* 38: 340-74. Jane Hicks Gentry's Jack Tales are reprinted in Betty N. Smith, *Jane Hicks Gentry: A Singer Among Singers* (Lexington: University Press of Kentucky, 1998), 106-34. Smith's book is an excellent source for students interested in the traditional songs and narratives of the Hicks-Harmon families passed on by a remarkable tradition bearer.

6. Richard Chase, ed., *The Jack Tales* (Boston: Houghton-Mifflin, 1943), title page. Houghton-Mifflin has printed numerous impressions of Chase's collection, and it is now available in paperback.

7. Thomas McGowan, "Beech Mountain Jack Tale," *Greenwood Encyclopedia of Folktales and Fairy Tales*, Vol. 1 (Westport, CT: Greenwood Press, 2008), 111-13. An excellent listing of books, recordings, and films on the Tales is included on the Ferrum University website <http://www.ferrum.edu/applit/>.

8. Two films show Orville Hicks driving Ray and Rosa Hicks to the National Storytelling Festival in Jonesborough, Tennessee, and helping them at home: *Ray and Rosa Hicks: The Last of the Old-Time Storytellers* (Charlotte, NC: Charles and Jane Hadley, 2000) and Luke Barrow's *My Life: I've Traveled the Mountains* (Derry, NH: Chip Taylor Communications, 1997).

9. *Orville Hicks: Mule Egg Seller and Appalachian Storyteller* (Boone, NC: Orville Hicks, 2004). CD is available from Orville Hicks, 142 Brown Farm Rd., Boone, NC 28607; 828-262-1551.

10. Richard Chase, ed., *Grandfather Tales* (Boston: Houghton-Mifflin, 1948), 234.

11. Gail E. Haley, *Mountain Jack Tales* (New York: Dutton Children's Books, 1992). Reprinted by Parkway Publishers.

12. Orville and Julia Ebel's collaboration have also produced an excellent collection of his family history and memories growing up: *Orville Hicks: Mountain Stories, Mountain Roots* (Boone, NC: Parkway Publishers, 2005).

In Orville's Words

When Orville Hicks tells his stories, he draws listeners into the mountain setting where he grew up—into Jack's world. The colorful language, passed down through mountain ancestry, brings an unequaled authenticity to Orville's tales. The speech is his own; he has no need to put on a storytelling voice.

With a simple, uncluttered beauty, this lively language tells stories about the mountain culture and stories about the storyteller who loves his mountain heritage. Orville's words and his pronunciations will be familiar to those who share his Appalachian roots. For those intrigued by words and regional language patterns, Orville's stories offer a rich field to explore.

REGIONAL SPEECH

Bear Waller: Bear Wallow; a bowl-like dip in the land, as if a bear had hollowed it out by wallowing there

bedad: a frequently used interjection, more intense than *well*, akin to *by golly*

bigger/weller enough: keeps *-er,* as in the comparative when used with *enough*

blar: briar

bound out: hired out. An orphaned child could be "bound out" to someone and would have to stay with that person and work for him. Also, a child could be "bound out" to work for someone, with money going to the child's parents in exchange for the child's work.

cloom: climbed

'em: shortened from *them* in running speech. When *them* is spoken with emphasis, the complete word is pronounced.

fall of the year: autumn

flitters: fritters; flour or meal cooked like pancakes

give out, gived out: tired, worn out

hand glider: hang glider

hew: to make or carve out of wood, as to "hew out a paddle."

holler: a hollow, a sheltered dip on the mountainside; also "holler log" for *hollow log*

knowed: knew

mans: men

nary: none, not

not nary: not at all, not any, none

off'n: off, off of (used as a preposition but not as an adverb)

old: emphasizes size ("big old house") or age ("old cabin"), or shows familiarity or fondness

old man: husband. *Old* can show fondness and familiarity at any age, so an "old man" could be young, as would be a "little old boy."

Old Pete: scarcity. A scarcity of food may be expressed by saying, "Old Pete is on the table."

old woman: wife. *Old* can show fondness and familiarity at any age, so an "old woman" could be young, as would be a "little old girl."

plumb: completely

poke: sack

put: went, as in "put through the woods."

rared back: reared back, leaning back

runt, run: ran

sody pop: soft drink, also called "sody dope"

sousing: soaking, washing

strop: stripe or strip

swarfed: swatted

'taters: potatoes

they was: often used for *there was* or for introductory words

took, took it: took off after; ran

throwed: threw

you'uns: *you*, when used as plural

PRONUNCIATIONS

at all: spoken as one word, *atall*; as for *not at all* (in text written as "not at-all")

ate: sometimes pronounced *et*

banjo: pronounced *banjer*

briar: pronounced *blar*

brother: pronounced *brüver*

chimney: pronounced *chimly*

donkey: pronounced *dunkey*

every: pronounced *ever*, as in "everbody" for *everybody* or "ever a girl" for *every girl*

fellow: pronounced *feller*

follow: pronounced *foller*

found: sometimes pronounced *fount*

fire: pronounced *far*

heard: pronounced *heared*

hire: pronounced *har*

hollow: pronounced *holler*, whether referring to a dip in the mountainside or a hollow log

it: pronounced as *hit* when stressed

Mast Store: pronounced *Mast-es Store*

old: often pronounced *ole* when used to show familiarity

pumpkin: pronounced *punkin*

says: pronounced with the long *a* of *say* plus *-s*

scared: pronounced as *skeered* or *skeert*

sword: pronounced with a voiced *w*

tusks: pronounced *tusk-es*

wing: pronounced *whing*

window: pronounced *winder*

GRAMMAR

a apple, a ax: *a* often used instead of *an* before a vowel sound

come, give, run: present tense verb used for past tense (*came, gave, ran*)

done: used as an auxiliary verb in the past perfect tense, as "done plumb forgot about" or "done plowed"

it wasn't: used to introduce a line, as, "It wasn't nothing there."

knowed, heared, etc.: addition of *-ed* often used to form past and past participle of irregular verbs

not nobody, not nothing, ain't never, ain't hardly nobody, etc.: double or multiple negatives used to express a single negative idea

them: used as a demonstrative pronoun pointing to a plural noun, as in "them galax" or "them blackberries" instead of *those galax leaves* or *those blackberries*

they was: spoken instead of *there was* when used as general introductory words: "They was seven flies in that puddle." *There was* still emphasizes location: "There was four of his apple trees chopped down," or "About three mile up the road there was a little old store." In this example, the standard pronunciation of *there* emphasizes its connection to location: "up the road there," not "there was a little old cabin."

For Further Thought

For Teachers, Students,
and Other Curious Folk

Passed-along Tales

As stories migrated from Europe, they kept some of their old framework yet took on elements of their new setting as well. How do Orville's stories reflect life in the mountains over the past few generations? Look for specific examples of mountain life in the stories.

What elements of European folktales appear in Orville's stories?
Why do you think that Orville's Jack Tales often include a king?

Read stories of "Cinderella," "The Brementown Musicians," and "The Three Billy Goats Gruff." Where do you find elements of these stories in Orville's stories?
Compare one of Orville's stories and a similar one from another source.

Look at other tellings of similar folktales. How do Orville's tellings differ? How are they the same?

"Catskin" is a Cinderella story. Read other Cinderella stories from other settings. What are the common elements of Cinderella stories? Which of these are present in "Catskin"?

Who is Jack? How would you describe Jack? Is his character consistent through the stories? If not, in which stories does his role differ? Why is Jack a folk hero? What makes Jack so likeable? How have stories such as these been valuable in mountain communities where they were told?

Why would a mountain mother pass them on to her children? Why would folks gather around a wood stove and tell tales they had heard often before?

Notice the repetition of ideas in the tales. Often a story groups three ideas: three challenging experiences, three people encountered, three events, etc. Why would folktales use groups of three? Why not use single elements—or groups of five or six? (Consider the aesthetics of three elements and the ease in remembering three points.) Notice how a story may even include two or more groups of three ideas.

Some stories develop through a sequence of similar events (Ex. "Soap, Soap, Soap"). What role does repetition play in these stories?

Oral tradition has deep roots. Many stories of religious heritage were told long before they were written. Even the stories of the Greek poet Homer were told orally many years before they were written. Learn about the role of oral tradition through history.

Consider the role of storytelling before the invention of the printing press with movable type around 1450.

Where in America, besides the Appalachian Mountains, have people told their stories orally? What do these stories tell about the lives of the storytellers? What role have oral stories played in the heritage of American Indians?

The Storyteller

Where do you hear elements of Orville's mountain experience in his stories? How do you think Jack is like Orville?

Orville Hicks draws listeners of all ages to his stories and holds their attention. What techniques make his storytelling so engaging?

Notice the use of active voice and the near absence of passive verbs in Orville's stories. Find examples of active verbs that give energy to these tales.

Listen to a recording of Orville's voice. What patterns do you notice in Orville's mountain speech? How does his speech affect the telling of the stories?

Finding Stories

Listen to the stories that persons around you tell. Do these stories reflect personal experience? Are these stories original? Are they passed along from an earlier generation?

Interview someone who grew up in an earlier generation. Make a list of questions to open conversation, but during the interview, look for ways to encourage and deepen conversation that evolves. Ask what stories this person remembers having heard.

Record a story as someone tells it. Try writing as the person talks. Try using a tape recorder and then transcribing the words. Be as accurate to the speaker's words as possible. Which approach is easier? What are the advantages and disadvantages of taping? What are the challenges you face in accurately transcribing someone's speech?

Telling Your Own Story

Tell a story of your own. You may write the story first, but tell it without reading it. Tell it again—and again, preferably on a different day. Was your story the same each time? Did you add anything? …change anything?

Have someone tell the story that you told. Did the new storyteller change the story? …add or omit details? …include a personal experience or viewpoint?

How is this storytelling experience similar to what has happened to folktales through the years?

How can you use voice and gestures to help tell a story?

Folksongs

Choose a familiar folksong. Use books, Internet, interview, or other sources to locate verses or versions of the song. How many different verses or versions can you find? Why have so many verses and versions been sung?

How are folktales and folksongs similar?

Simpler Times: Venues for Storytelling

Turn off the television, the computer, the cell phone, the electronic games, the CD player—anything that distracts, anything that operates on electricity or batteries. Sit and talk with family or friends on the porch, around a table, by a fire—some quiet place.

If you grew up in a time and place without electrical and technological devices, you would not miss them. How would life be different?

Work together on a simple manual task—a household task, such as snapping beans, or a creative project, such as knitting. What other tasks could you do together? Enjoy the conversation and the stories that are shared. Share stories of the past, dreams for the future.

Mountain Speech

Read the section "In Orville's Words" at the back of the book. Find examples in the text of his regional speech patterns.

Listen to a recording of Orville Hicks or of Ray Hicks. Notice the pronunciations and rhythms of the words. How are Orville's and Ray's voices similar, and how do they differ?

What words, expressions, or pronunciations give flavor to the speech in your area? Collect local expressions or sayings from your region.

How does mobility of our population affect language patterns? What effect do the various forms of media (radio, television, motion pictures, etc.) have on local language patterns? Are the effects positive or negative? How so?

Orville In Books
& Recordings

Books:

Ebel, Julia Taylor. *Orville Hicks: Mountain Stories, Mountain Roots*. Boone, North Carolina: Parkway Publishers, 2005.

Isbell, Robert. *The Keepers: Mountain Folk Holding on to Old Ways and Talents*. Winston-Salem, North Carolina: John F. Blair, 1999. A chapter and the cover photo feature Orville Hicks.

CD:

Hicks, Orville. *Orville Hicks: Mule Egg Seller and Appalachian Story Teller*. Recordings: Boone, North Carolina: Orville Hicks, 1998. Liner notes: Boone, North Carolina: Thomas McGowan, 1998. CD reissued in 2004 with the addition of "The Ballad of Ray Hicks" and Orville's reflections on Ray Hicks.

Video:

The Jack Tales Festival 2002 (with other storytellers). Blowing Rock, North Carolina: Jack Tales Festival, 2002.

Audio Cassettes:

Hicks, Orville. *Carryin' On: Jack Tales for Children of all Ages*. Whitesburg, Kentucky: June Appal Recordings, 1990.

Hicks, Orville. *Orville Hicks: Mule Egg Seller and Appalachian Storyteller*. Recordings: Boone, North Carolina: Orville Hicks, 1998. Liner notes: Boone, North Carolina: Thomas McGowan, 1998.

Magazines and Newspapers:

Orville Hicks has been featured in numerous magazines and newspapers, including *Our State*, *North Carolina Folklore Journal*, *Smoky Mountain Living*, *High Country Magazine*, *The Watauga Democrat*, and *The Mountain Times*.

Awards and Honors:

Kentucky Colonel Award, 1990.

Brown-Hudson Folklore Award, 1997, North Carolina Folklore Society.

North Carolina Heritage Award, 2007, North Carolina Arts Council.

Tellebration, Best All-around Liar Award, 2008, Watauga Arts Council.

Paul Green Multi-Media Award, 1999, for the CD *Orville Hicks: Mule Egg Seller and Appalachian Story Teller*, North Carolina Society of Historians.

Willie Parker History Book Award, 2006, for *Orville Hicks: Mountain Stories, Mountain Roots*, as told to Julia Taylor Ebel, North Carolina Society of Historians.

Smithsonian Folklife Festival, 2003, Washington, DC.

One North Carolina Festival, 2005, governor's inaugural celebration, Raleigh, North Carolina.

Stories for Life Festival, 2007, Piccolo Spoleto Festival, Charleston, South Carolina.

What People Say About Orville

"Orville Hicks tells Jack Tales, riddles, jokes, ghost stories and tall tales passed down to him and adds his own personal experiences to the mix. A 2007 recipient of the North Carolina Heritage Award, Orville is a godsend for those who love Appalachian culture and yearn to hear mountain storytelling practiced masterfully in the present day."

–Wayne Martin, Folklife Director,
North Carolina Arts Council

"One thing I will always remember about Orville is his wonderful laugh. Sometimes he gets so tickled while telling a story that he can barely go on. His pure joy and deep love of his art form—the telling of these ancient, precious stories—that he so willingly shares with the rest of us. That's what makes Orville priceless!"

–Hawk Hurst, storyteller and friend

"Orville is Orville, and he's the best storyteller I've ever heard in my life."

–Richard Tester, long-time friend

"We never miss an opportunity to hear Orville Hicks tell his tales, and although we've heard them dozens of times, they are ever fresh and attention riveting. We love his contagious chuckling throughout his stories and childhood anecdotes, confirming that he is enjoying himself as much as we are enjoying him."

–The Rev. Ernest & Miriam Haddad

"Orville and I have been friends for over 20 years. I have enjoyed doing programs with him. He is a wonderful storyteller and a wonderful person. I am pleased that he was given the North Carolina Heritage Award in 2007. He is one of the youngest to receive that award, but people realized that he is extraordinary."

–Glenn Bolick, potter, storyteller, friend

"Orville is a humble being with a generous spirit. His stories reflect a culture that is deep and rich and a traditional lifestyle that few of us will ever know."

–Doug Elliott, naturalist, storyteller, and author of
Wildwoods Wisdom and *Wild Roots*

May the stories live on

in the voice of Orville Hicks,

in the voices of storytellers everywhere.

JULIA TAYLOR EBEL celebrates nature, heritage and cultural history through stories and poetry. Her books include *Orville Hicks: Mountain Stories, Mountain Roots*; *Addie Clawson: Appalachian Mail Carrier*; *Walking Ribbon*; and most recently, *Dresses, Dreams and Beadwood Leaves*. The earlier three received North Carolina Society of Historians book awards. Over 50 of her nature poems are published in children's magazines. Julia leads programs and workshops on keeping stories and on poetry. She lives in Jamestown, North Carolina, but a part of her heart is in the North Carolina mountains, where she finds inspiration for much of her writing.

www.JuliaEbel.com

SHERRY JENKINS JENSEN has shared her art as a mural artist and as the illustrator of *Addie Clawson: Appalachian Mail Carrier*. A North Carolina native and graduate of the University of North Carolina at Greensboro, she lives in Greensboro with her husband and three active sons.